MENSA®

PRESENTS

MIGHTY MINDBUSTERS

This edition published by Barnes & Noble Inc.,
by arrangement with Carlton Books Limited.

Barnes & Noble Books 1997

ISBN 0-7607-0532-1

Printed and bound in Italy

MENSA®
PRESENTS
MIGHTY
MINDBUSTERS

John Bremner & Carolyn Skitt

BARNES
&NOBLE
BOOKS
NEW YORK

AMERICAN MENSA LTD

American Mensa Ltd is an organization for individuals who have one common trait: an IQ in the top 2% in the nation. Over 50,000 current members have found out how smart they are. This leaves room for an additional 4.5 million members in America alone. You may be one of them.

Looking for intellectual stimulation?

If you enjoy mental exercise, you'll find lots of good "workout programs" in the Mensa Bulletin, our national magazine. Voice your opinion in one of the newsletters published by each of our 150 local chapters. Learn from the many books and publications that are available to you as a member.

Looking for social interaction?

Are you a "people person," or would you like to meet other people with whom you feel comfortable? Then come to our local meetings, parties and get-togethers. Participate in our lectures and debates. Attend our regional events and national gatherings. There's something happening on the Mensa calendar almost daily. So, you have lots of opportunities to meet people, exchange ideas, and make interesting new friends.

Looking for others who share your special interest?

Whether yours is as common as crossword puzzles or as esoteric as Egyptology, there's a Mensa Special Interest Group (SIG) for it.

Take the challenge. Find out how smart you really are. Mensans love to read so you already have something in common.

Contact American Mensa Ltd today and ask for a free brochure. We enjoy adding new members and ideas to our high-IQ organization.

American Mensa Ltd
201 Main Street, Suite 1101
Fort Worth, Texas 76102

INTRODUCTION

At Mensa we spend a lot of time coming up with puzzles of ever more fiendish complexity. Not satisfied with making people solve one puzzle at a time we invented the Mind Maze in which puzzles are linked in a chain with the answer to one leading you to the next challenge. Now it's time for a return to some good old-fashioned simplicity. Our first two books in this series were Word Puzzles and Number Puzzles and those titles have traveled the globe and enjoyed outstanding success. Now we have followed them up with the imaginatively(!) named New Word Puzzles and New Number Puzzles. The best news is that in this combined volume you can try them both. So here they are: nearly 400 examples of straightforward puzzling fun. Even so, I bet you chew your way through a few pencils before you finish!

If you would like to join Mensa contact us at American Mensa Limited, 2626 E 14th Street, Brooklyn, New York 11235-3992, USA, or the address opposite. British Mensa Limited is at Mensa House, St John's Square, Wolverhampton, WV2 4AH England, or contact Mensa International, 15 The Ivories, 628 Northampton Street, London N1 2NY, England who will be happy to put you in touch with your own national Mensa.

R. P. Allen

Robert Allen
Editorial Director
Mensa Publications

CONTENTS

NUMBER PUZZLES

Number puzzles are perennially popular and such was the response to our last volume that it came as no surprise when the publisher demanded more. To bring a fresh feel to the project we have engaged a new author, John Bremner, whose skill at designing entertaining and stimulating puzzles is matched only by the boundless energy he brings to the task. John, I can confidently predict, will ensure that your mathematical skills are tested to the limit.

In this volume, as in many of the previous Mensa puzzle books, we have been fortunate in having the editorial services of David Ballheimer, himself a puzzler of awesome abilities. Our thanks to him for his many hours of checking and revising the proofs. Also we would like to thank our Series Editor, Liz Wheeler, and Series Art Editor, Paul Messam, who minister in a kind of guardian angel capacity over the entire series.

If you enjoy these puzzles you would enjoy Mensa. There you can meet people from all walks of life but of similar brain power. Mensa is quite simply a wonderful social club which spans the world and allows people with intellectual interests to get together for their mutual benefit and entertainment. There are 120,000 Mensans throughout the world, so why not join us? See the previous pages for details of how to join.

R. P. Allen

Robert Allen
Editorial Director
Mensa Publications

Insert the missing numbers. In each pattern the missing number has something to do with the surrounding numbers in combination.

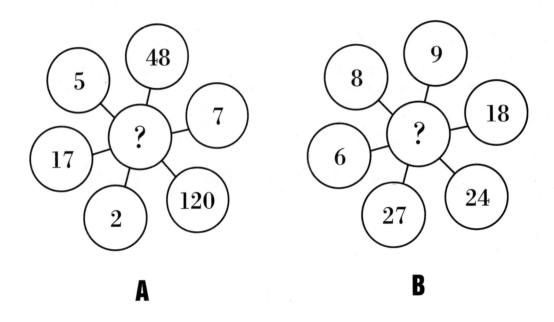

A   **B**

SEE ANSWER 44

PUZZLE 2

If Picasso is worth 28 and Monet is worth 22, how much is Raphael worth?

SEE ANSWER 83

Take a five-digit number and reverse it. Subtract the original number from its reverse, and you are left with 33957. What was the original number?

SEE ANSWER 35

What number should replace the question mark?

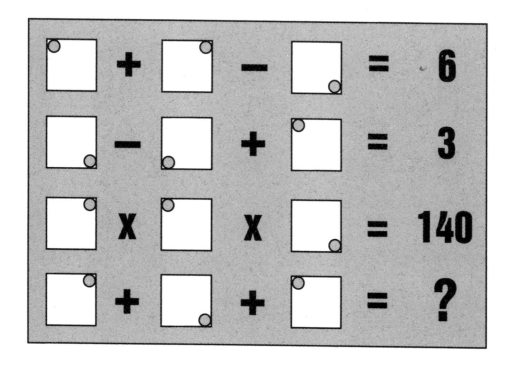

SEE ANSWER 50

Za-za is older than Fifi, but younger than Juan. Fifi is older than Jorjio and Maccio. Maccio is younger than both Carlos and Jorjio. Juan is older than both Fifi and Maccio, but younger than Carlos. Who is the oldest, and who is the youngest?

SEE ANSWER 61

PUZZLE 6

When the shaded sections of this puzzle are brought together, one of the white patches is inserted into the middle to make a magic square in which all rows, columns and long diagonals add to 49. Is it patch A, B, C or D?

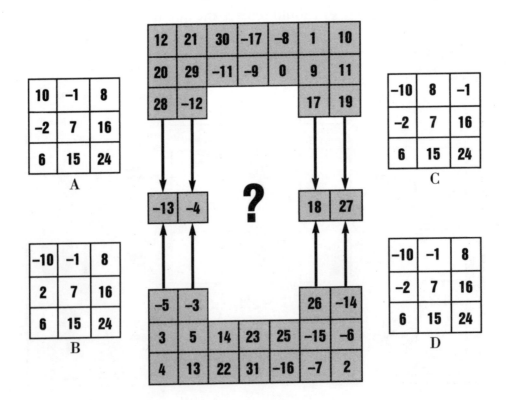

SEE ANSWER 75

A rectangular swimming pool of constant depth is twice as long as it is wide, but the owner is unhappy with the dimensions of the pool. The length is reduced by 12 units and its width increased by 10 units. When this is done, the modified pool will hold exactly the same volume of water. What were the pool's original dimensions?

SEE ANSWER 23

PUZZLE 8

Each shape is made up of two items, and each same shape has the same value, whether in the foreground or background. What number should replace the question mark?

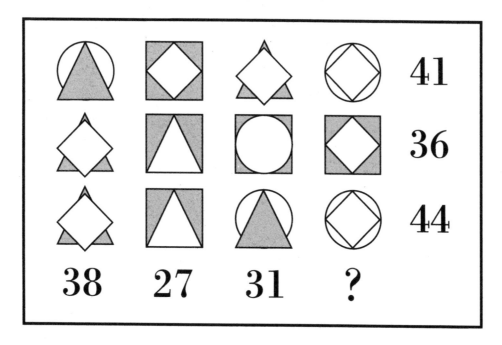

SEE ANSWER 33

PUZZLE 9

What is the area of the shaded path, if the path is one unit wide?

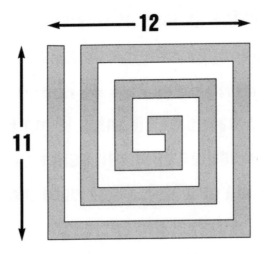

SEE ANSWER 46

PUZZLE 10

The panel below, when complete, contains the binary numbers from 1 to 25. Does binary patch A, B, C or D complete the panel?

1	1	0	1	1	1	0	0	1	0	1
1	1	0	1	1	1	1	0	0	0	1
0	0	1	1	0	1	0	1	0	1	1
1	1	0			?			1	1	1
0	1	1						0	0	1
0	0	0						0	1	0
0	1	1	1	0	1	0	0	1	0	1
0	1	1	0	1	1	0	1	0	1	1
1	1	1	0	0	0	1	1	0	0	1

1	0	1	1	1
1	1	1	1	0
1	1	1	0	0

A

0	1	1	0	1
1	1	1	0	0
0	1	0	0	1

B

1	1	0	1	1
1	1	0	1	1
0	0	1	0	1

C

0	1	1	0	1
1	1	1	0	0
1	1	0	0	1

D

SEE ANSWER 17

Which letters, based on the alphanumeric system,
should go into the blank boxes?

6	1	7	3				5	1	3	9				2	2	9	2		
1	3	5	4	A	H	B	2	8	6	4	F	B	C	4	3	0	9		
7	7	0	9				8	6	2	6				7	1	7	8		

SEE ANSWER 55

What number, when you
multiply it by 5 and add 6,
then multiply that result by 4
and add 9, gives you a number
that, when you multiply it by
5 and subtract 165, gives you a
number that, when you knock
off the last 2 digits, brings you
back to your original number?

SEE ANSWER 84

PUZZLE 13

What number should replace the question mark?

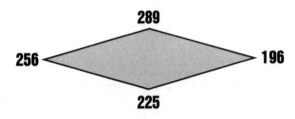

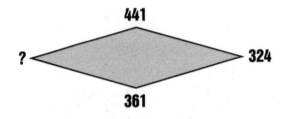

SEE ANSWER 76

PUZZLE 14

If each large ball weighs one and a third times the weight of each little ball, what is the minimum number of balls that need to be added to the right-hand side to make the scales balance?

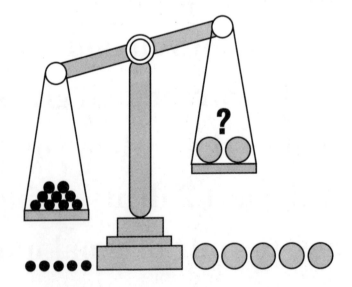

SEE ANSWER 6

PUZZLE 15

Present at Juan's birthday party were a father-in-law, a
mother-in-law, a daughter-in-law, two sons, two daughters, two
sisters and a brother, four children, three grandchildren, two
fathers, two mothers, a grandfather, and a grandmother.
However, family relationships can be complicated.
One man's brother can, of course, be another man's
brother-in-law, and at the same time, someone's son.
With that in mind, what is the smallest number of people
needed at the party for the above relationships to exist?

SEE ANSWER 27

PUZZLE 16

How many rosettes are missing from the blank circle?

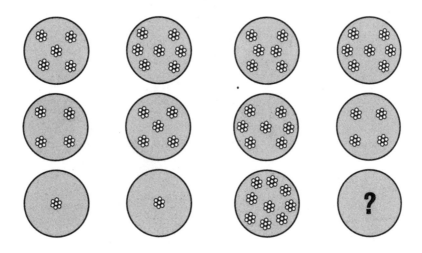

SEE ANSWER 85

Forty people took part in a freestyle race. Twenty people ran. Ten people dashed. Five people bolted and sprinted. Three people bolted, dashed, ran and sprinted. Two people ran, bolted, and sprinted. Five people ran and sprinted. Two people dashed, ran, and sprinted. How many people neither dashed, ran, bolted, nor sprinted?

SEE ANSWER 69

PUZZLE 18

What value needs to go into the upper box to bring this system into balance? Note: The beam is broken down into equal parts and the value of each box is taken from its midpoint.

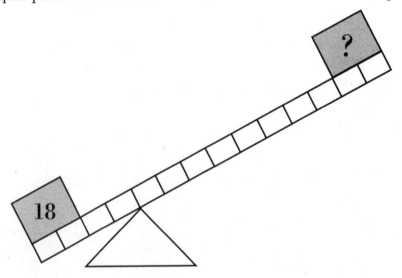

SEE ANSWER 41

PUZZLE 19

Find a route from the top of this puzzle to the bottom that arrives at the total 353, always going down and to an adjoining hexagon.

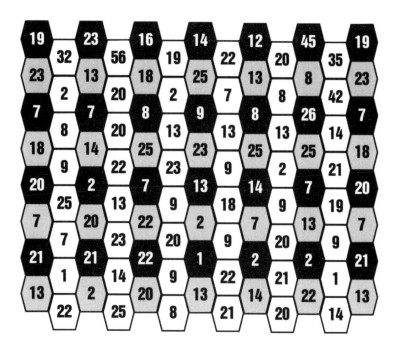

SEE ANSWER 15

PUZZLE 20

Using only the numbers already used, complete this puzzle to make all the rows, columns, and long diagonals add to 27.

6				
			2	
	9			
				3
		7		

SEE ANSWER 21

PUZZLE 21

Insert the supplied rows of numbers into the appropriate places in the grid to make all rows, columns and long diagonals add to 17. Example: (C) goes into the location (a).

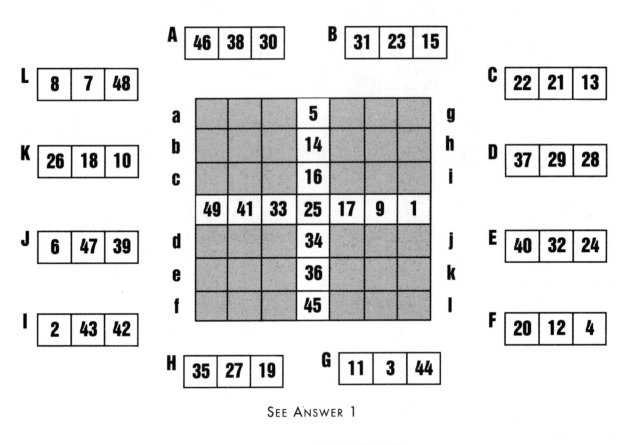

A | 46 | 38 | 30

B | 31 | 23 | 15

L | 8 | 7 | 48

C | 22 | 21 | 13

K | 26 | 18 | 10

D | 37 | 29 | 28

Grid values (centre column top to bottom): a 5, b 14, c 16; middle row: 49, 41, 33, 25, 17, 9, 1; d 34, e 36, f 45

J | 6 | 47 | 39

E | 40 | 32 | 24

I | 2 | 43 | 42

F | 20 | 12 | 4

H | 35 | 27 | 19

G | 11 | 3 | 44

SEE ANSWER 1

PUZZLE 22

At 3pm one day, a flagpole and a measuring pole cast shadows as shown. What length is the flagpole?

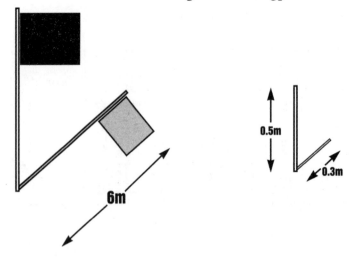

SEE ANSWER 34

PUZZLE 23

Use logic to discover which shape has the greatest perimeter.

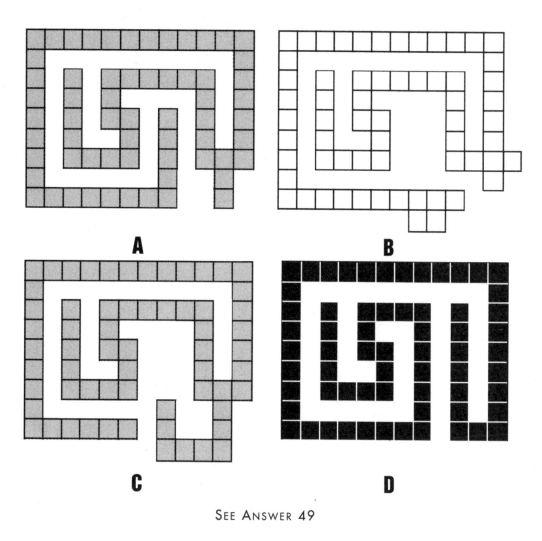

A

B

C

D

SEE ANSWER 49

PUZZLE 24

Crack the code to find the missing number.

A	B	C	D	E	F	G	H	I	J
9	3	8	7	8	9	2	8	5	7
1	2	1	5	?	7	1	0	1	2
K	L	M	N	O	P	Q	R	S	T

SEE ANSWER 70

What number should replace the question mark?

6 8 4 8 7 9 6 ?

SEE ANSWER 36

PUZZLE 26

Which number replaces the question mark?
What is the value of each animal?

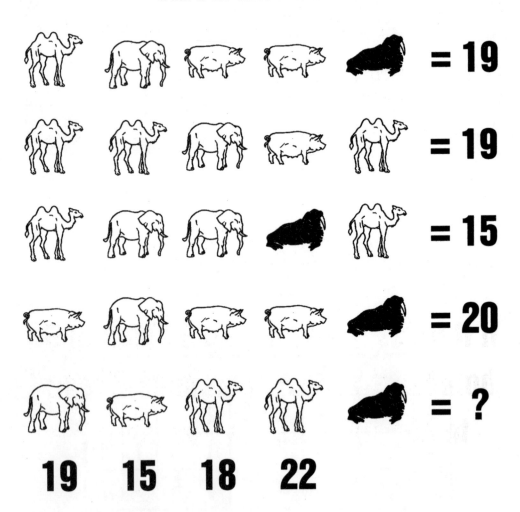

19 15 18 22

SEE ANSWER 13

What number should replace the question mark?

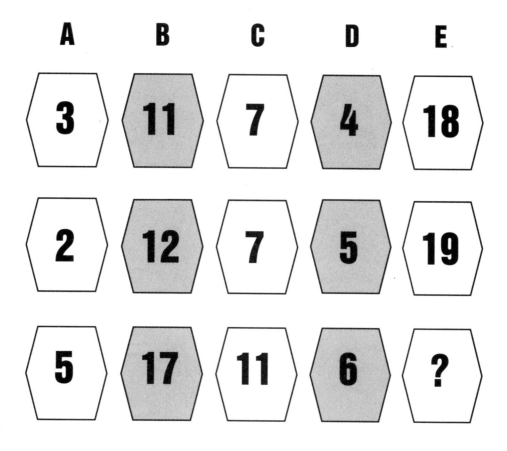

SEE ANSWER 32

PUZZLE 28

If it takes 5 men to dig 5 holes in 5 hours, how many men does it take to dig 100 holes in 100 hours?

SEE ANSWER 72

PUZZLE 29

Put the right number in the blank star.

SEE ANSWER 22

PUZZLE 30

If you buy 9 barrels of beer for 25 Credits each, but you are given a 25% discount on the last 4 barrels, and you are given in change 3 times the cost of all the barrels less half the value that your discount would be if your discount were 25% more for the last 2 barrels than the discount you were actually given, what was the total cost of the barrels ?

SEE ANSWER 9

Starting from any square on the top row, you can accumulate points by stepping down diagonally to another, adjoining square, and adding that to your total. You may not land on a square containing the number one, or on any square horizontally adjacent to a square with a one, but you may start from such a square.

You may not travel up or sideways. By continuing this process until you reach a square on the bottom row, what is the maximum number of points it is possible to accumulate?

9	4	5	3	6	1	8	2
8	1	2	2	3	2	5	1
6	9	9	1	2	4	3	5
4	8	1	3	5	2	6	1
1	4	3	7	6	3	1	4
9	2	4	8	6	4	5	3
4	2	9	4	8	6	7	1
2	8	1	6	5	9	0	1

SEE ANSWER 37

When a ball is dropped from a height of 9 m, it bounces back two-thirds of the way. Assuming that the ball comes to rest after making a bounce which takes it less than 2 mm high, how many times does it bounce?

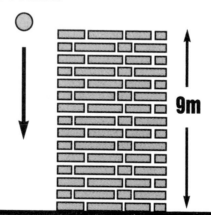

9m

SEE ANSWER 66

25

The planet Pento is inhabited by a race of highly intelligent one-toed quadrupeds with elephant-like trunks. So with four toes and a trunk, they have adopted the five base for their number system. With that in mind, convert the Pento number 1234 into its decimal equivalent.

SEE ANSWER 42

PUZZLE 34

Which number should replace the question mark?

$$❄ + ☕ - ☀ = 6$$
$$❄ \times ☕ \times ☀ = 30$$
$$❄ - ☕ - ☀ = 0$$
$$❄ + ☕ + ☀ = ?$$

SEE ANSWER 28

PUZZLE 35

These systems are in balance. What weight is required in
the right hand box to balance the load ?

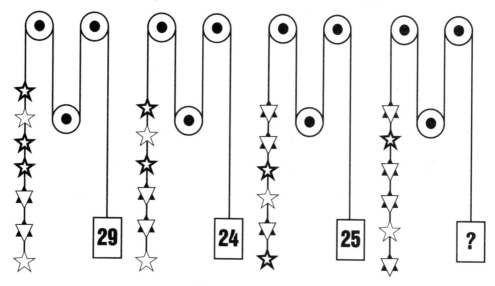

SEE ANSWER 54

PUZZLE 36

Each same shape has the same value. What number should
replace the question mark

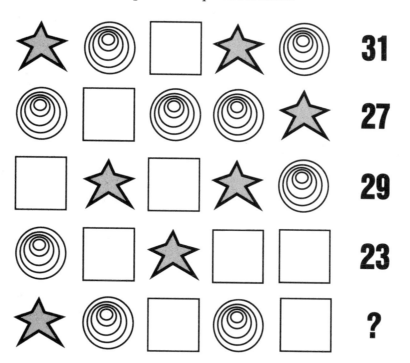

★	◎	□	★	◎	31
◎	□	◎	◎	★	27
□	★	□	★	◎	29
◎	□	★	□	□	23
★	◎	□	◎	□	?

SEE ANSWER 82

Find the missing number.

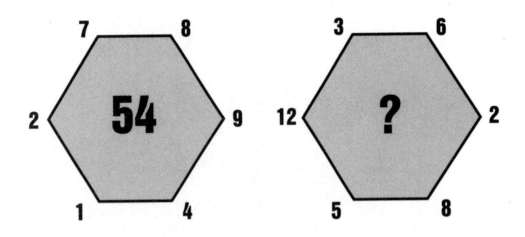

SEE ANSWER 8

PUZZLE 38

What three-digit number should replace the question mark?

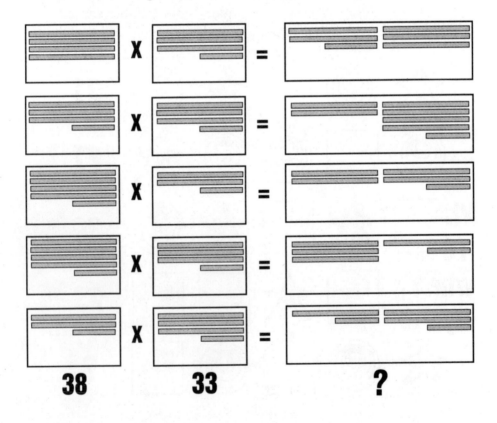

38   33   ?

SEE ANSWER 77

PUZZLE 39

The three balls at the top of each hexagon should contain numbers that, when added together and subtracted from the total of the numbers in the three balls at the bottom of each hexagon, equal the number inside each relevant hexagon. Insert the missing numbers.

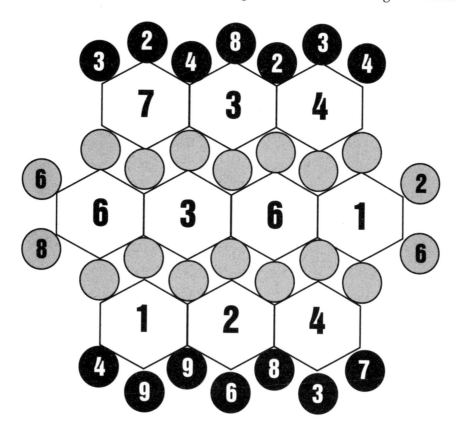

SEE ANSWER 58

PUZZLE 40

What number, when added to a number 10 times as big, gives a number that, when its right-hand digit is multiplied by four and added to the result of the above, gives 1000?

SEE ANSWER 12

What number should replace the question mark?

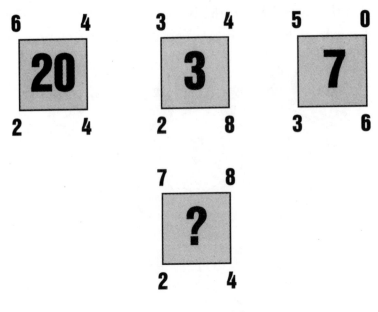

SEE ANSWER 38

PUZZLE 42

This clock has been designed for a planet that rotates on its axis once every 16 hours. There are 64 minutes to every hour, and 64 seconds to the minute. At the moment the time on the clock reads a quarter to eight. What time, to the nearest second, will the clock say the time after the next time the hands appear to meet?

SEE ANSWER 25

PUZZLE 43

A large sheet of paper is 0.1 mm thick. A man amuses
himself by tearing it in half and putting both pieces together,
and then tearing those into four sheets, and repeating the
process until he has done it twenty-five times.
How high is the stack of paper now?

a) As thick as a book   b) As high as a man   c) As high as a house
d) As high as a mountain

SEE ANSWER 29

PUZZLE 44

This is a time puzzle. Which symbol is missing ?
Is it A, B, C, D, E or F?

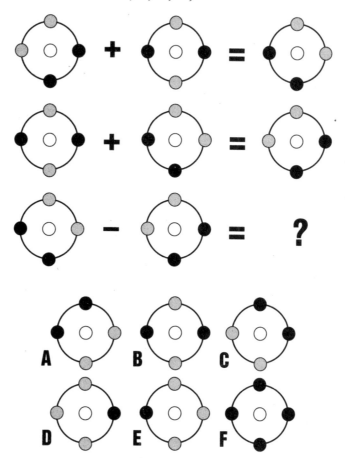

SEE ANSWER 81

Which number should replace the question mark?

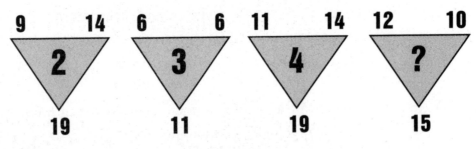

SEE ANSWER 16

PUZZLE 46

Insert in the boxes at the corner of each shaded number-square, the digits which are multiplied together to give the numbers in the shaded boxes. For example, in the bottom left corner, 144 is derived from 3 x 6 x 8 (and another multiplier – here 1), but you also have to consider how this helps to make solutions for the surrounding numbers… and so on.

3		5		4		4		3		3
	90		120		64		144		54	
2										1
	48		96		16		72		36	
1										2
	160		80		20		150		30	
4										1
	180		10		40		100		15	
9										3
	27		8		32		12		81	
3										9
	24		28		84		45		135	
8										1
	144		42		63		225		25	
3		6		1		3		5		1

SEE ANSWER 64

What number should replace the question mark?

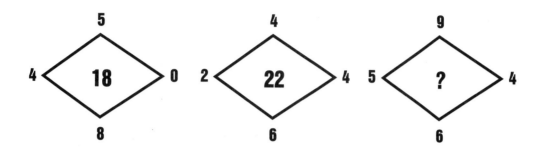

SEE ANSWER 40

PUZZLE 48

Each like symbol has the same value. Supply the missing total.

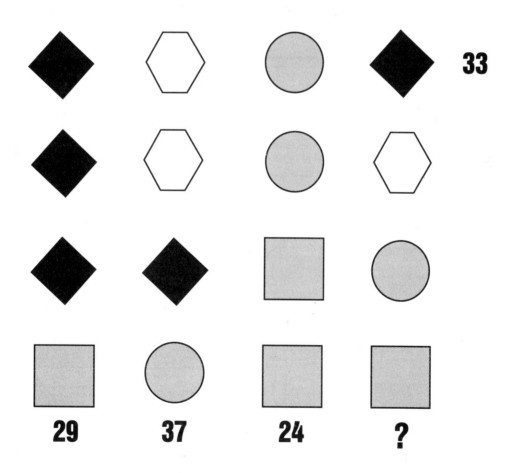

SEE ANSWER 3

What time will it be, to the nearest second, when the hands of this clock next appear to meet?

SEE ANSWER 11

PUZZLE 50

What number should replace the question mark?

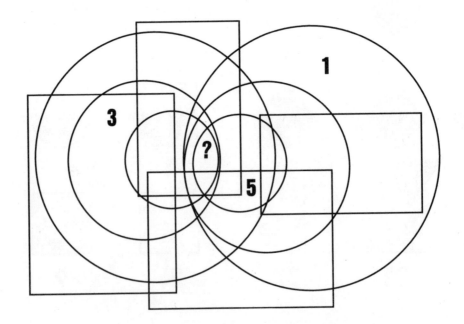

SEE ANSWER 31

Insert the missing numbers in the blank hexagons.

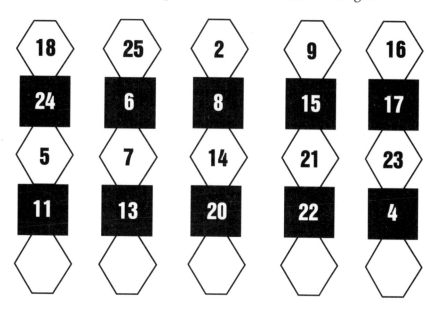

SEE ANSWER 62

What number should replace the question mark?

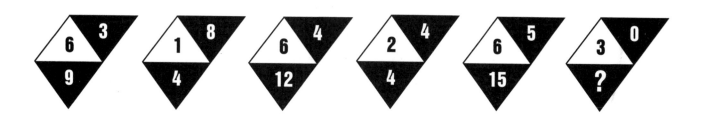

SEE ANSWER 56

What number should replace the question mark?

9	7	2	5	7	4	3	2	5	1
									4
9	4	5	2	7	5	2	7		5
3							9		9
6		?	2	6	5	1	8		8
2									1
8	3	5	2	7	4	3	3	6	5

SEE ANSWER 73

PUZZLE 54

Black counters are nominally worth 4.
White counters are nominally worth 3.
Being on a diagonal trebles a counter's value.
Being on the innermost box doubles a counter's value.
Being on the outermost box halves a counter's value.
The rules work in combination.
What is the total value of all the counters on the board?

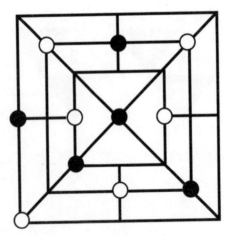

SEE ANSWER 43

What number continues the sequence?

SEE ANSWER 20

PUZZLE 56

I have a deck of cards from which some are missing. If I deal them equally between nine people, I have two cards to spare. If I deal them equally between four people, I have three cards to spare. If I deal them between seven people, I have five cards to spare. There are normally 52 cards in the deck.

How many are missing?

SEE ANSWER 47

PUZZLE 57

Each same symbol has the same value. What number should replace
the question mark?

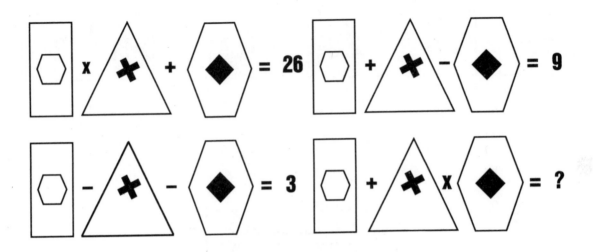

SEE ANSWER 74

PUZZLE 58

What number should replace the question mark?

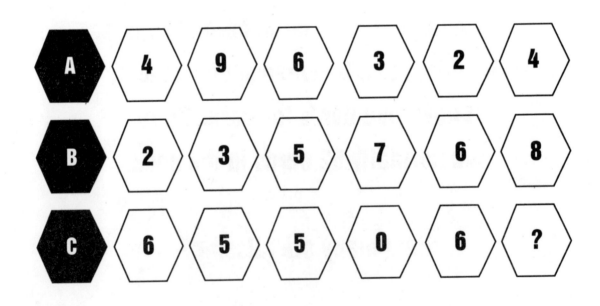

SEE ANSWER 53

PUZZLE 59

What number should replace the question mark in the blank square?

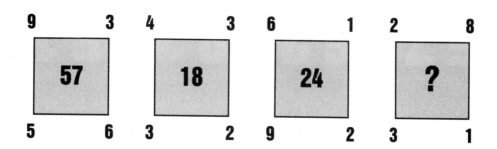

SEE ANSWER 19

PUZZLE 60

Insert the central numbers.

A

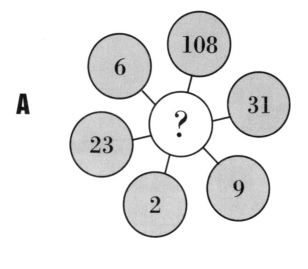

B

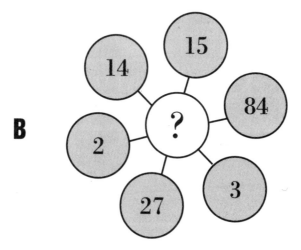

SEE ANSWER 4

PUZZLE 61

The load on this beam and rollers apparatus has to be moved a distance of 20 units. If the circumference of each of the rollers is 0.8 units, how many turns must the rollers make to accomplish the move?

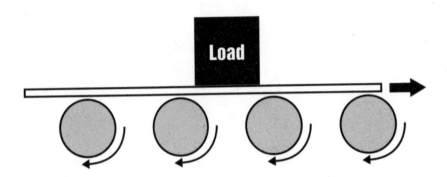

SEE ANSWER 45

PUZZLE 62

Insert the numbers supplied into the puzzle grid.
There is only one correct way.

ACROSS

118	916	3052	9481
155	951	3184	9857
200	0193	5056	16659
277	0360	5119	35677
293	1048	5832	51719
390	1066	6073	56151
653	1918	7176	76891
724	2390	7775	6036300
915	2983	8885	~~7424361~~

DOWN

08	5667	72612	897511
49	7900	87333	965853
63	8659	95138	3704058
66	8890	116765	4756628
69	10875	215810	6754451
90	50713	353637	229137152
4920	62817	675856	248143773
5086			

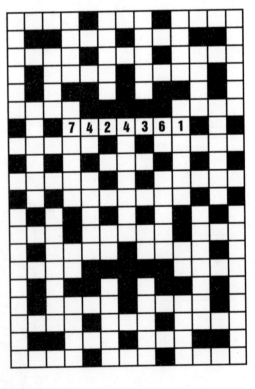

SEE ANSWER 57

PUZZLE 63

What number should replace the question mark?

SEE ANSWER 48

PUZZLE 64

The symbols represent the numbers 1 to 9.
Work out the value of the missing multiplier.

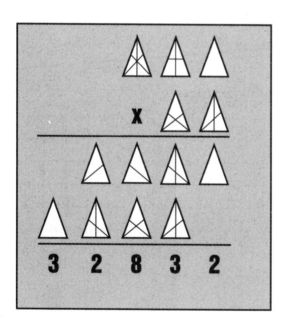 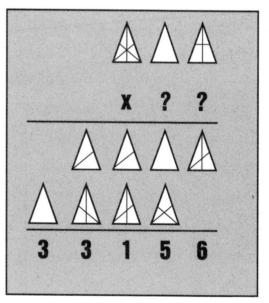

SEE ANSWER 51

This system is balanced. How heavy is the black box (ignoring leverage effects)?

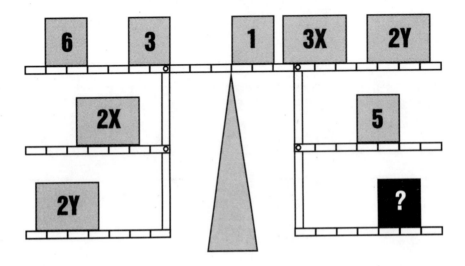

SEE ANSWER 86

Somewhere within the numbers below left, there is a number that, if
it is put into the grid below, starting at the top left and working
from left to right, row by row, will have the middle column as shown
when the grid is completed. Put in the missing numbers.

30958672356978091239485 66
80941641622234563412191 83
62161444327089298461529 55
00162193200025281312158 58
71939450463951231617621 13
26779228965612310223840 46
12898540432616142526160 93
41728583009124285964813 42
56830998012847306133902 1

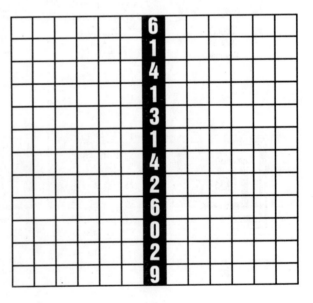

SEE ANSWER 60

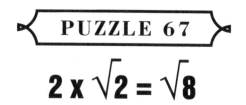
$$2 \times \sqrt{2} = \sqrt{8}$$

$$3 \times \sqrt{5} = \sqrt{45}$$

What number should replace the question mark?

$$4 \times \sqrt{6} = \sqrt{?}$$

SEE ANSWER 2

PUZZLE 68

The black, white and shaded rings of this square target always have the same value, irrespective of their position, and each target is worth 44. Which of the targets, A, B, C or D, will replace the question mark?

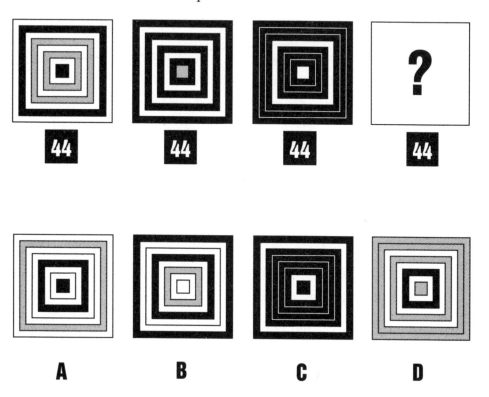

A   B   C   D

SEE ANSWER 30

How many different ways is it possible to arrange the order of these four kings?

SEE ANSWER 65

PUZZLE 70

Find this famous historical date.

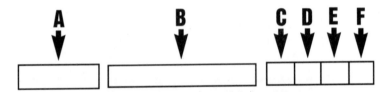

A. The two digit number that, when you divide it by two and add one, then square the result, gives a number that when you subtract one and divide it by ten, gives you twelve.

B. The month that comes three months after the month that comes seven months before the month that is a month before the month that comes nine months after March.

C. The number that, when you square it, add the result to itself, and multiply the result of that by ten, gives you the date in A.

D. The number that, when you square it and add both of the resulting digits together, brings back your original number.

E. The number that, when you add four and multiply the result by ten, gives a number that when added to the original number plus two, and divided by four, gives twenty-seven as a result.

SEE ANSWER 18

If the top left intersection is worth 1, and the bottom right
intersection is worth 25, which of these nodule grids,
A, B, C or D, is worth 67?

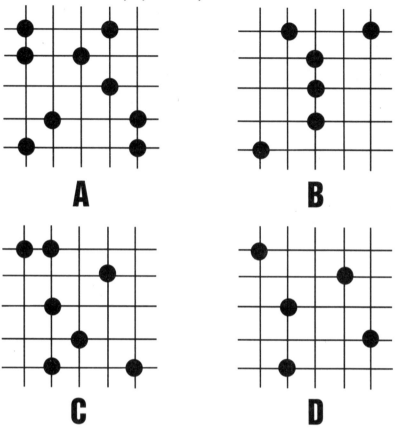

SEE ANSWER 79

Previous to the time shown, when were all four
of the digits on this watch last on display?

SEE ANSWER 67

Each like shape has the same value. Which is the missing symbol?

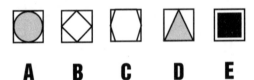

A   B   C   D   E

SEE ANSWER 26

PUZZLE 74

Find within the number below, two numbers, one of which is double the other, and which when added together make 10743.

57162383581

SEE ANSWER 14

This system is balance. How heavy is the black weight
(ignoring leverage effects)?

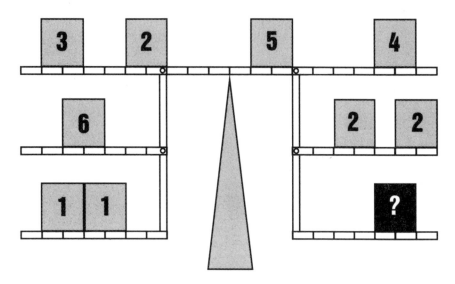

SEE ANSWER 24

PUZZLE 76

There are logical differences in the way each of these squares
work, but they all involve simple addition or subtraction of rows.
What are the missing numbers?

A

2	6	3	0	8	a
3	8	0	3	9	b
2	3	?	5	7	c
1	9	2	5	4	d
2	1	5	3	6	e

B

2	1	3	2	0	a
1	3	5	6	2	b
0	5	?	4	7	c
2	9	6	3	0	d
1	0	2	9	9	e

C

3	1	2	0	9	a
6	1	4	6	2	b
2	8	?	1	9	c
4	9	6	5	7	d
7	1	3	3	3	e

D

3	3	6	4	7	a
3	3	6	1	1	b
1	1	?	2	0	c
3	4	1	0	6	d
2	1	9	3	2	e

SEE ANSWER 71

What number should replace the question
mark in the third hexagon pattern?

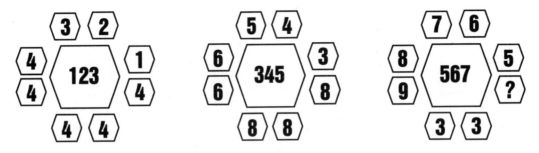

SEE ANSWER 59

PUZZLE 78

Fill the numbers into the blank spaces. There is only one correct way.

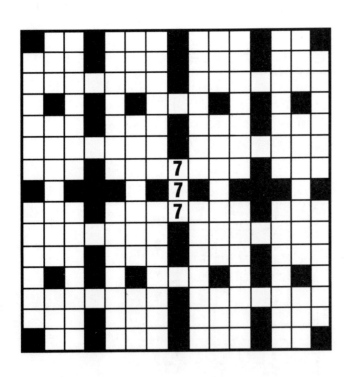

ACROSS

29	345	477	1052151
47	389	485	1285465
58	394	488	1469451
81	409	510	1779317
012	416	550	2008732
018	437	563	2457149
048	439	746	2857375
142	448	775	5125721
192	459	819	5418409
314	473	907	9588859

DOWN

138	777	1949159	6656485
198	158453	2193241	7413313
231	219952	2443740	8475941
250	420417	3854345	8614451
410	590579	4112340	8724315
473	0474542	5984178	9855707
745	1274458	6584404	9905865
750			

SEE ANSWER 7

The squares of the times it takes planets to go round their sun are proportional to the cubes of the major axes of their orbits. With this in mind, if CD is four times AB, and a year on the planet Zero lasts for six earth years, how long is a year on the planet Hot?

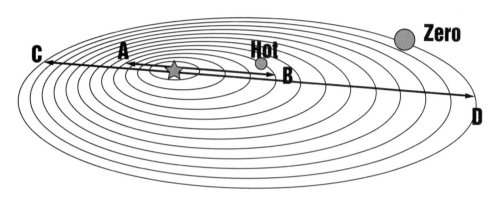

SEE ANSWER 68

PUZZLE 80

Put the stars into the boxes in such a way that each row is double the row below.

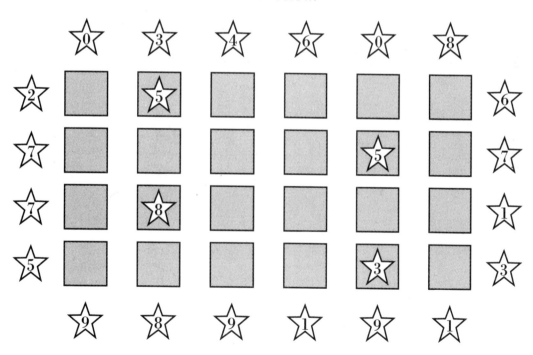

SEE ANSWER 10

Which is the odd number out?

Thirty-six
Sixty-four
Seventy-two
Twenty-five
Eighty-one

SEE ANSWER 63

PUZZLE 82

What number should replace the question mark?

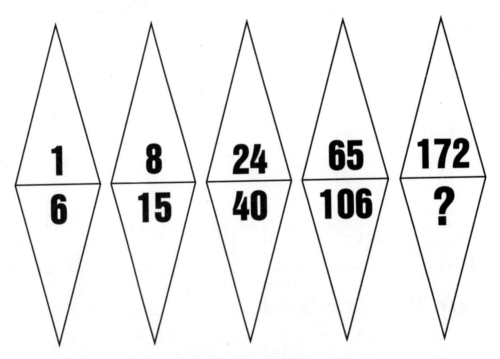

SEE ANSWER 80

Insert the missing numbers to make each row, column,
and long diagonal add to 189.

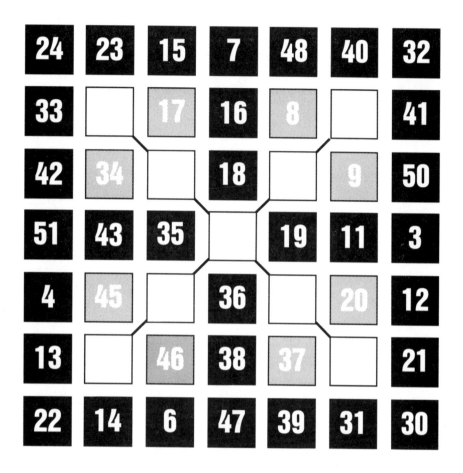

SEE ANSWER 52

PUZZLE 84

In 1952, New Year's Day was on a Tuesday. What day of the week was New Year's Day in 1953?

SEE ANSWER 5

Find two numbers, contained within the number below,
which give 8647492 when multiplied together.

6 5 8 8 7 2 1 4

SEE ANSWER 78

⊣ PUZZLE 86 ⊢

What number should replace the question mark?

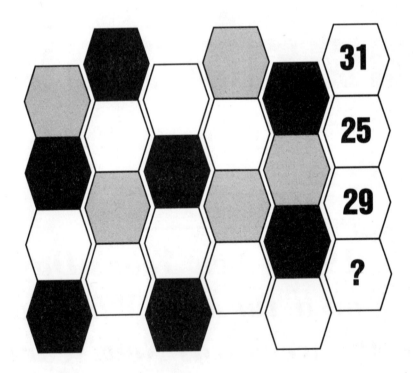

SEE ANSWER 39

What is the missing number?

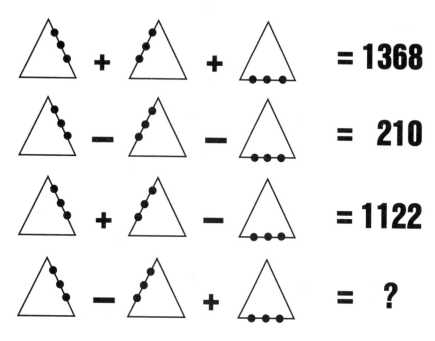

SEE ANSWER 121

PUZZLE 88

Five of these numbers interact together to give the number 1 as a solution. Which five numbers, and in which order?

+ 19	x 9	+ 29	x 7	– 999
– 94	+ 173	+ 65	– 236	x 8
+ 122	x 5	x 212	+ 577	– 567
+ 190	x 6	x 4	– 435	x 22
x 13	– 87	x 12	– 172	+ 117

SEE ANSWER 182

The number below, when the digits are rearranged and multiplied by 63, produces a particularly repetitive result. What is the new number and what is the result?

1 7 3 4 9 6 5 2

SEE ANSWER 110

PUZZLE 90

Jon is Lorraine's brother. Diane married Jon. Diane is John's sister. Lorraine married John. Diane and Jon had seven grandchildren. Diane and Jon had three children. Lorraine and John had two children. Lorraine and John had seven grandchildren. Ricardo, one of Diane and Jon's children, and a cousin to Lorna-Jane and Frazier, did not marry, and had no offspring. Diane and Jon had two other children – Juan and Suzi. Lorraine and John had two children – Lorna-Jane and Frazier. Lorna-Jane married Juan, and had four children. Frazier married Suzi and had three children. Lorraine and John had twins. Frazier and Juan were cousins. Suzi and Lorna-Jane were cousins. Ricardo had a sister. Lorna-Jane had a brother. Frazier had a sister. Suzi had two brothers. For the above relationships to exist, how many were there, grandparents, parents, children, cousins and siblings in all?

SEE ANSWER 138

PUZZLE 91

Map the alphabet into two rows to work out the value
of N and hence P.

F = 25	O = 17	L = 37	P = N + 4

SEE ANSWER 87

PUZZLE 92

Decode the logic of the puzzle to find the missing number.

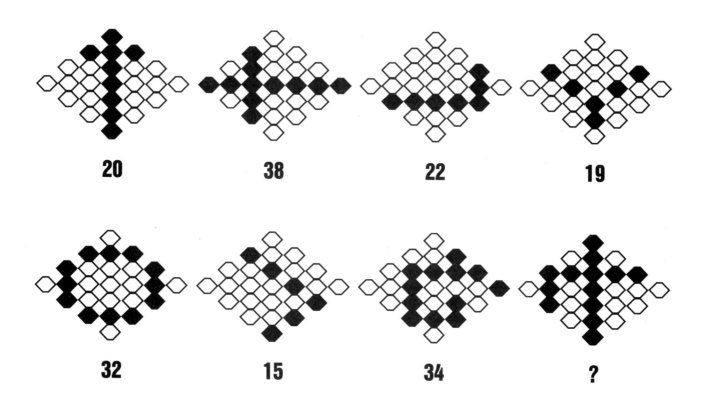

20   38   22   19

32   15   34   ?

SEE ANSWER 103

Insert the columns into the appropriate places to make both long diagonals add to 182.
The middle column, (D), has been done for you.

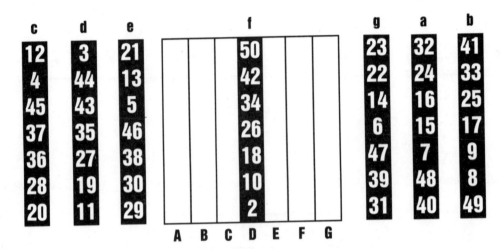

A	B	C	D	E	F	G

SEE ANSWER 134

What is the missing number?

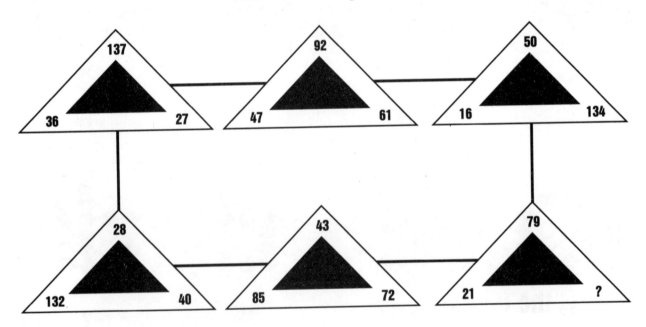

SEE ANSWER 176

These systems are in balance. What is the missing number?

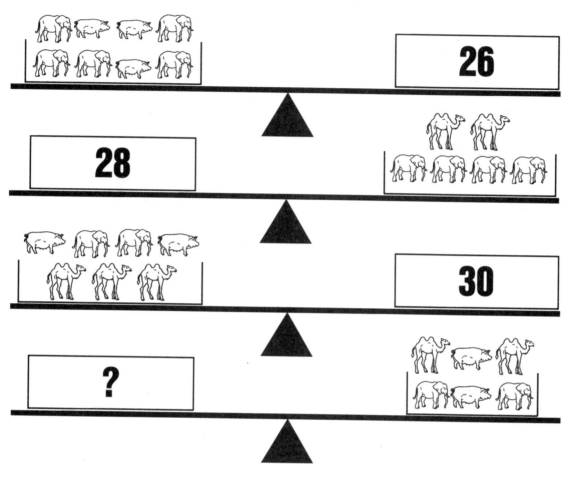

SEE ANSWER 159

PUZZLE 96

Find this 6-digit number.
First 3 digits – last 3 digits = 665. Within
the number there is a 3 to the left of a 1.
There is a 0. There is a 7 to the right of a 9.
There is a 5 to the left of a 3.

SEE ANSWER 104

What is the missing number?

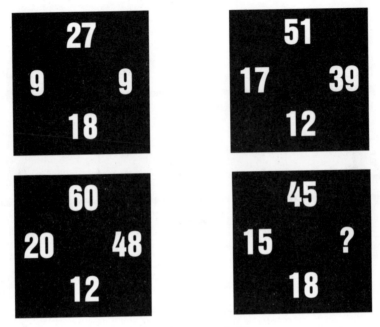

SEE ANSWER 160

Put the appropriate number on the blank balloon.

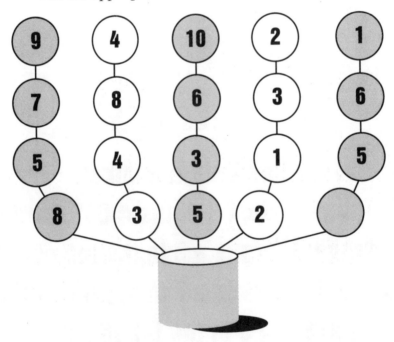

SEE ANSWER 167

Fill in the blanks for Espresso.

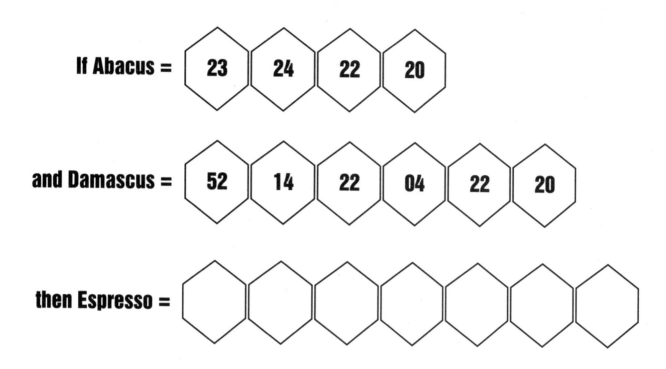

If Abacus = 23 24 22 20

and Damascus = 52 14 22 04 22 20

then Espresso =

SEE ANSWER 156

What is the largest number you can write with three digits?

SEE ANSWER 122

What is the missing number?

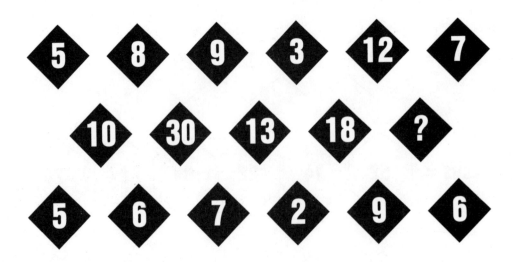

SEE ANSWER 183

PUZZLE 102

What is the missing number?

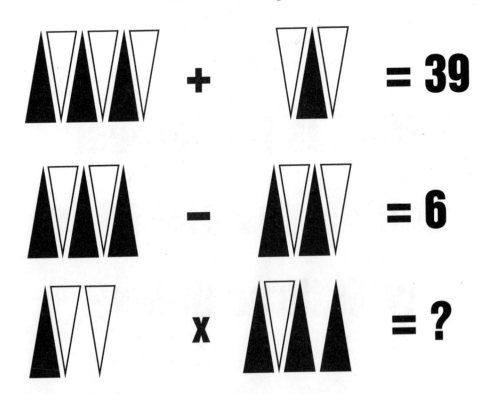

SEE ANSWER 111

60

What 6-figure number, found within 3691428570, when multiplied by every number between 1 and 6, results in a number with the same digits rearranged each time?

SEE ANSWER 139

⟨ PUZZLE 104 ⟩

Which of the supplied tiles, A, B, C, D, E or F, logically fits into the vacant space?

A
8	8	2
2	9	2
4	7	1

B
2	8	2
1	8	1
4	7	2

C
2	8	2
1	8	1
4	7	1

2	9	3	7	3	2	1	1	8	
		5	4	3	8	4	2	4	2	0
8	3	5	6	6	3	0	2	4	
		7	2	9	2	4	1	8	1	4
6	4	7	4	4	2	8	2	4	
		7	2		?		1	6	1	4
6	2	9	2	6			2		
		3	9				2	8	2	7
3	4	5	4	8	2	0	1	2	
		2	8	6	3	2	1	8	1	6
2	9	4	6	6	2	4	1	8	
		7	6	8	6	4	8	4	2
5	5	9	3	2	2	7	2	5	

D
2	8	2
2	9	2
4	7	1

E
2	8	2
1	9	1
4	5	1

F
3	8	3
1	8	1
4	7	1

SEE ANSWER 88

PUZZLE 105

Five armadillos = two pigs

One pig + one cat = one dog

One armadillo + one cat = one horse

Four pigs + two armadillos = two dogs

Four horses + three dogs = five cats + seven pigs + one armadillo

If armadillos are worth 2, what are the values of the
dogs, horses, cats and pigs?

SEE ANSWER 155

PUZZLE 106

In the blank hexagon at the corner of each black box, write a
single-digit number which, when added to the other three corner
numbers, equals the total in the middle. For example, 25 could be
5 + 5 + 6 + 9. But you have to consider how the surrounding totals,
20, 19, and 21, will be affected by your choice. You must use each
number – including 0 – at least once.

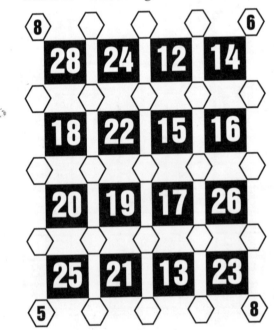

SEE ANSWER 135

PUZZLE 107

What is the missing number?

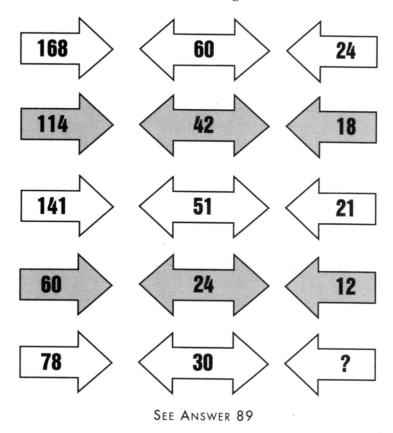

168	60	24
114	42	18
141	51	21
60	24	12
78	30	?

SEE ANSWER 89

PUZZLE 108

Put the appropriate number in the blank triangle.

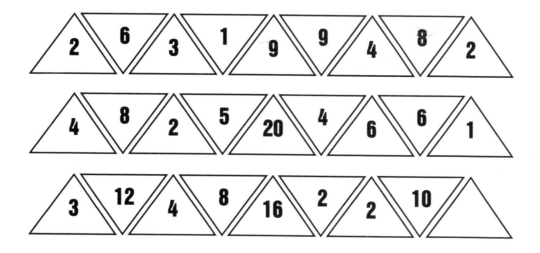

2 6 3 1 9 9 4 8 2

4 8 2 5 20 4 6 6 1

3 12 4 8 16 2 2 10

SEE ANSWER 105

Find the continuous sequence of 76384 in the grid below,
starting from the top row and ending on the bottom row.
You may go along or down, but not up or diagonally.
The numbers are not all in a straight line.

```
7 7 8 7 8 7 3 7 6 3 8 7
6 6 6 6 4 6 7 6 3 3 4 6
3 3 3 8 3 3 3 8 4 8 3 3
8 4 8 4 7 8 3 8 6 4 7 8
3 7 3 7 3 4 7 4 7 3 4 4
3 6 3 6 8 3 4 3 6 3 8 4
7 3 7 3 8 4 8 6 8 4 7 4
7 8 7 8 4 8 7 6 7 4 3 8
8 3 8 3 7 7 4 3 3 6 7 3
3 7 4 7 6 3 4 8 7 3 3 4
7 8 7 8 3 3 7 4 7 6 3 4
3 4 3 4 7 3 3 8 3 7 8 4
4 3 4 3 6 7 7 3 4 8 3 7
7 4 7 4 4 3 4 3 3 8 3 6
8 3 8 3 7 4 3 8 4 4 7
```

SEE ANSWER 136

Hidden within the number below are two numbers which, when
multiplied together, produce 1111111111111111.
What are they?

6513594777124183

SEE ANSWER 161

Complete the analogy.

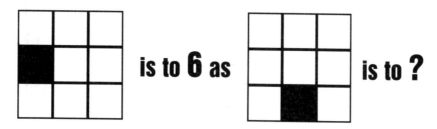

SEE ANSWER 123

Fill the numbers into the blank spaces. There is only one correct way.

ACROSS

118	2133	6289
126	2345	6321
149	2801	9134
197	2803	9277
421	3458	9783
738	3482	12304
769	3485	12334
823	4190	12345
864	4227	53802
932	4656	56182
987	5199	0693878
1366	5660	9124914

DOWN

14	8228	443628
15	9998	492660
25	12735	536293
33	15787	593680
39	17151	4143383
42	24991	5428292
1178	26114	6132104
2119	64843	586713226
3002	116357	981921603
6334	200900	

SEE ANSWER 147

The only symbols that concern you in this multiplication puzzle are stars. Using their positions on the grid, calculate the missing number.

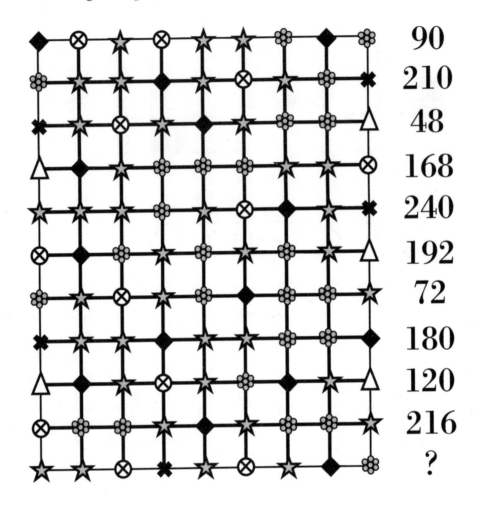

90
210
48
168
240
192
72
180
120
216
?

SEE ANSWER 168

PUZZLE 114

Fill in the blank squares.

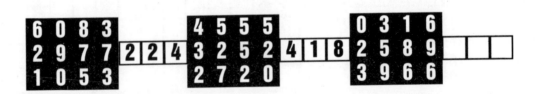

SEE ANSWER 184

What is the missing number?

SEE ANSWER 112

This system is balanced. How heavy is the black box (ignoring leverage effects)?

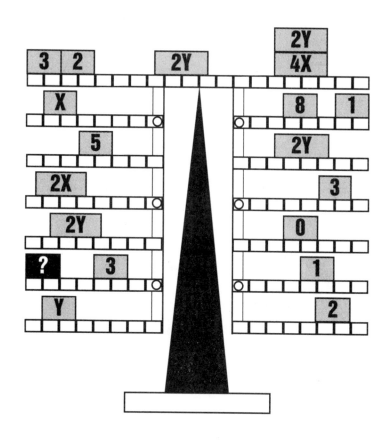

SEE ANSWER 140

PUZZLE 117

Each like shape has the same value.
Which shape should replace the question mark?

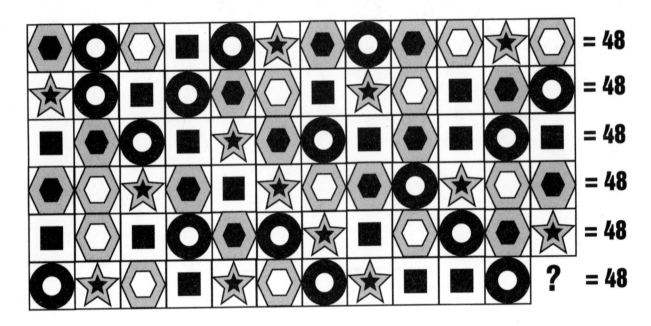

= 48
= 48
= 48
= 48
= 48
? = 48

A   B   C   D   E

SEE ANSWER 185

PUZZLE 118

What is the value of the right-hand target?

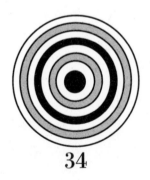  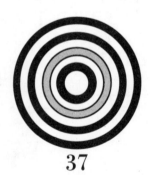 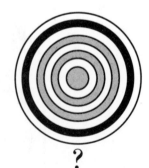

34   36   37   ?

SEE ANSWER 113

An architect, after drawing plans for a room, finds that if he increases the length of the room by two units, and reduces the width by one unit, while maintaining the same height of ceiling, the room will have the same volume. If the difference between the original dimensions was three units, what were the length and breadth of the room on the original drawing?

SEE ANSWER 141

PUZZLE 120

Use three straight lines to divide this square into five separate sections containing a total of 52 in each.

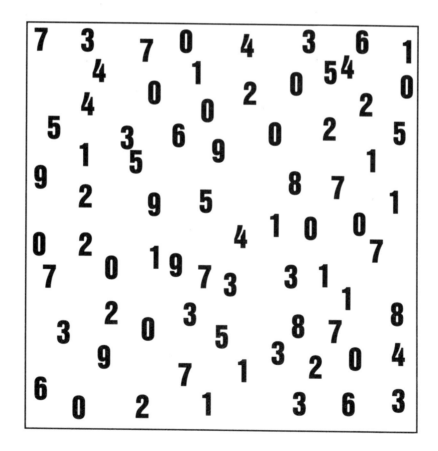

SEE ANSWER 90

In four moves of two pieces, make two numbers of alternating backgrounds, such that when you subtract one from the other, the result is 671. You must not finish with any gaps between the numbers but they will occur as you work through the puzzle.

SEE ANSWER 106

PUZZLE 122

What is the missing number?

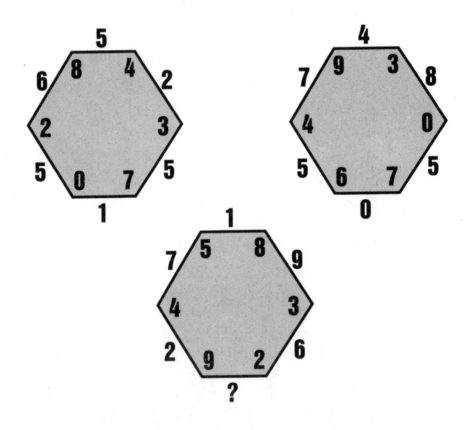

SEE ANSWER 127

PUZZLE 123

Which two numbers below, when you put them together and multiply the result by one of the other numbers, produces 12345678 as a result?

21 43 65 990 453 7765 8213 8890 6 5578 34 44
6012 05476 8653 9963 3257 45 75 25 2057 43567
7833 301 2134 248 54 79 92 12 38 22387 457 908
98 3245 1144 0980 356 76 91 111 88 2345 905 1121
42 5567 233 2355 8807 5467 890 20 994 1123 4356
7879 4567 67844 86743 54389 33 22 89 345665
052340 76435 345 120 243 94 123 100 53 400 335
555 613 1200 695443 2332 567 1023 845 77 325 205

SEE ANSWER 162

PUZZLE 124

The numbers in the three balls above each cell, when multiplied together, minus the value of the numbers in the three balls below each cell, when multiplied together, is equal to the value of the numbers inside each cell. Insert the missing numbers.

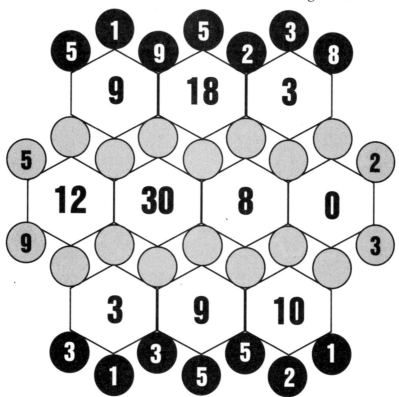

SEE ANSWER 169

PUZZLE 125

Insert the missing number.

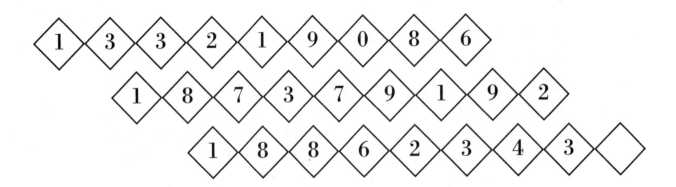

Row 1: 1 3 3 2 1 9 0 8 6
Row 2: 1 8 7 3 7 9 1 9 2
Row 3: 1 8 8 6 2 3 4 3 □

SEE ANSWER 148

PUZZLE 126

If each large ball weighs three units, what is the weight of each small black ball? A small white ball has a different weight from a small black ball. All small balls are solid; both the large balls are hollow.

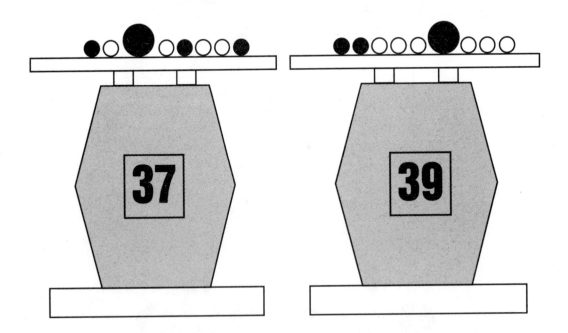

SEE ANSWER 124

PUZZLE 127

Each like symbol has the same value. What number should replace the question mark?

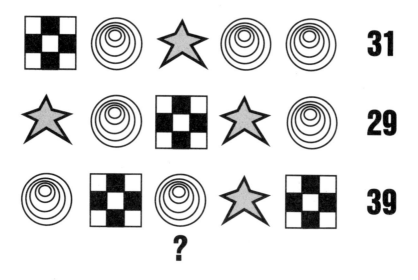

SEE ANSWER 170

PUZZLE 128

Insert the missing value in the blank square.

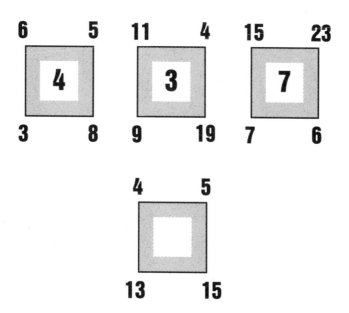

SEE ANSWER 149

Which two numbers, when multiplied together, give a result that, when added to itself, produces a number that, when the digits are added together, has a solution that gives the same result as the original two numbers added together and, if doubled, produces the same result as the original two numbers multiplied together?

SEE ANSWER 125

◄ PUZZLE 130 ►

What is the missing number?

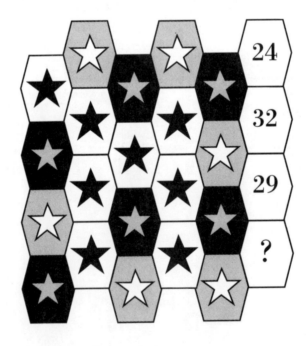

SEE ANSWER 186

PUZZLE 131

Fill the numbers into the grid. They only fit one way.

ACROSS

69	263	726	1761670
76	328	751	4256701
84	338	758	4971467
97	447	778	5231937
092	450	821	6368906
096	472	847	6579804
101	517	930	6596817
122	627	957	7062502
131	650	974	7554403
147	660	0379304	8369591
167	692	1062387	9511198
171	697	1291762	9512209
178	706	1518117	9974515
239	711	1751171	

DOWN

069	298915	1028507	7057147
106	412961	1508171	7081701
352	497811	1970788	7097230
353	517268	2567039	7097429
379	576816	3374277	7121176
461	584605	3602976	7607138
513	709656	4298164	7632154
573	720412	4650786	7948137
590	797991	5247127	8076467
126959	862178	5364561	9912061
162717			

The grid contains the pre-filled entry **8 4 7**.

SEE ANSWER 114

PUZZLE 132

Put a value from below into each triangle so that the total in each square gives a value that makes each row, column, and long diagonal add to 203.

6 8 29 9 27 30 13

7 3 29 14 15 8 3

2 19 11 12 39 0

40 1 7 11 2 9 2

34 13 10 8 12 20

19 36 5 4 5 18 40

SEE ANSWER 142

Insert the missing number in the blank square.

9	8
1	2

4	0
2	5

6	2
4	

5	5
4	9

8	2
3	4

7	1
2	3

SEE ANSWER 91

PUZZLE 134

What is the missing number?

SEE ANSWER 97

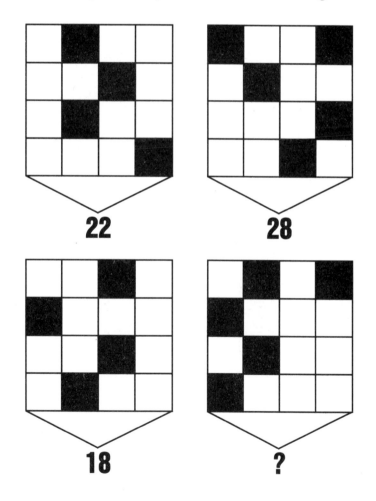

Express a half, using all the digits from one to nine.

SEE ANSWER 128

PUZZLE 136

Decode the logic of the puzzle to find the missing number.

22   **28**

18   **?**

SEE ANSWER 163

What are the individual values of the black, white and shaded hexagons.

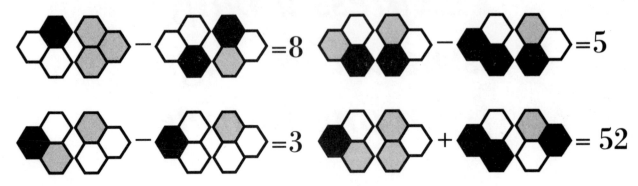

SEE ANSWER 98

```
102249384746098712345466883471294887625545
447011231350157612086925281802795398700917
293538920102603916707176981599565032900307
291807780769785326089299120291707719783009
103250525167289629096091385079909850329109
910782736456970823655423109846739290904622
```

Somewhere within the number above, there is a number which, if put into the grid below, starting at the top left and working from left to right, row by row, will have the middle column as shown when the grid is completed. Put in the missing numbers.

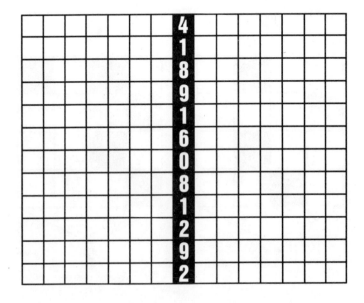

SEE ANSWER 129

Find within this number, a 6-digit number which, when divided by three gives a 5-digit palindromic number. (The number is the same reading from the left and the right.)

1 3 9 1 4 0 5 9 2 1

SEE ANSWER 164

⊰ PUZZLE 140 ⊱

The planet Spectra is widely known this side of the galaxy for its interesting inhabitants and large families. Zeebob and Gobop keep track of their family by classifying them according to certain physical characteristics, with most offspring belonging in more than one classification group. There are 18 offspring with green self-replicating fingers; 17 with three purple peppermint toes; 11 with red glowing eyes and blue hair; and 16 with luminous hypno-teeth of irresistible charm.

Looking at shared characteristics, 5 of those with three purple peppermint toes have red glowing eyes and blue hair; 5 of those with three purple peppermint toes have luminous hypno-teeth of irresistible charm, and 5 of those with three purple peppermint toes have green self-replicating fingers. Of those with red glowing eyes and blue hair, 5 have three purple peppermint toes, and 3 have luminous hypno-teeth of irresistible charm. Of those with luminous hypno-teeth of irresistible charm, 6 have green self-replicating fingers; 5 have three purple peppermint toes, and 3 have red glowing eyes and blue hair. Of those with green self-replicating fingers, 5 have three purple peppermint toes, and 6 have luminous hypno-teeth of irresistible charm. One member of the family can be classified under either green self-replicating fingers; three purple peppermint toes, or luminous hypno-teeth of irresistible charm. Two members of the family can be classified under either luminous hypno-teeth of irresistible charm; three purple peppermint toes, or red glowing eyes and blue hair.

How many offspring do Zeebob and Gobop have?

SEE ANSWER 171

Complete the analogy.

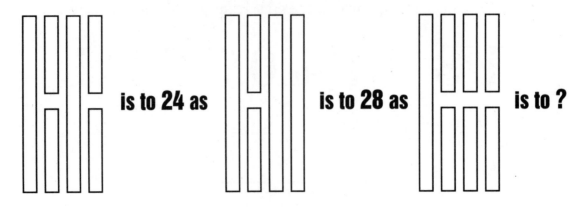

is to 24 as ... is to 28 as ... is to ?

SEE ANSWER 150

Only the value of the positions of the black boxes in each column are added to give the number at the bottom (the numbers in the white boxes are a further clue). Work out the logic to find the value of the question mark.

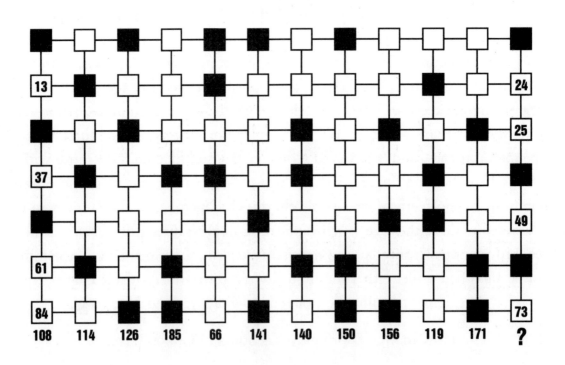

SEE ANSWER 126

What is the missing number?

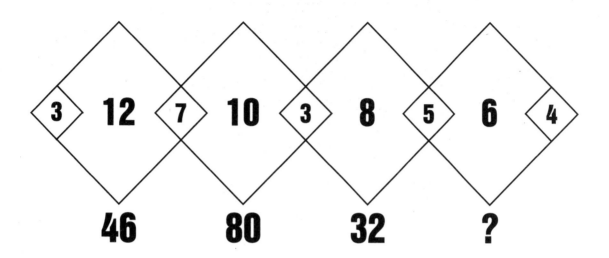

46   80   32   ?

SEE ANSWER 177

PUZZLE 144

Which of these four sets is the odd one out?

1	9	0	3	3
0	3	3	1	9
	1		0	

4	2	8	1	1
8	1	1	4	2
	4		8	

3	0	9	2	2
9	2	2	3	0
	3		9	

2	4	3	5	5
5	5	2	4	3
	3		5	

3		9		3
9	0	3	3	1
3	3	1	9	0

A

1		2		1
2	8	1	1	4
1	1	4	2	8

B

2		0		2
0	9	2	2	3
2	2	3	0	9

C

4		5		2
5	2	4	3	5
3	5	5	2	4

D

SEE ANSWER 115

Find a route from the top to the bottom of this puzzle that gives 175 as a total. Any number adjacent to a zero reduces your total to zero.

SEE ANSWER 143

How many bacteria cultures should be in the Petri dish with the question mark?

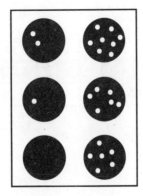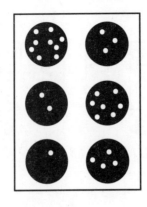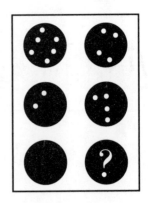

SEE ANSWER 92

Insert the appropriate value in the blank triangle.

SEE ANSWER 116

Which 2-digit number, the values of which when added together total 10, will always divide exactly into any 8-digit number in which the first four digits are repeated in the second half in the same order?

SEE ANSWER 144

PUZZLE 149

If it takes twelve men two hours to dig a hole two feet long by two feet wide by two feet deep, how long will it take six men to dig a hole twice as long, wide and deep?

SEE ANSWER 93

PUZZLE 150

121938161	298561129	593734058	713213284
187828984	373954020	622992359	825861951
215442670	417262383	731874334	842522382
258901049	530289165	751287578	964582595
270127824	573762717	770017983	989893113

Locate the position of the numbers in the box above on the grid below. You may travel in any direction, but the lines have to be straight and no numbers are missed out.

```
5 5 9 3 3 1 2 1 7 9 8 5 2 7 9
5 2 1 7 3 8 5 1 2 8 5 3 5 0 6
1 7 1 8 1 4 3 9 5 6 0 1 0 5 0
2 0 3 8 9 2 8 7 1 4 2 9 2 0 7
6 1 9 7 1 5 3 9 3 8 4 5 3 6 2
5 2 7 3 6 2 8 1 7 9 8 2 4 9 0
1 7 2 1 8 2 1 5 2 9 5 3 6 0 7
5 8 1 9 0 3 7 9 0 7 3 4 2 7 5
4 2 7 3 9 8 2 1 3 4 5 1 0 7 0
9 4 5 8 7 2 0 6 7 8 3 0 7 2 2
4 3 9 0 2 4 3 8 2 4 1 7 5 1 0
0 8 1 5 9 8 1 5 6 7 9 6 3 8 7
9 5 3 4 7 3 9 2 9 4 1 8 1 9 7
0 2 5 1 7 5 1 8 3 0 5 4 0 3 5
8 1 0 3 8 1 3 0 4 1 3 6 1 7 6
```

SEE ANSWER 99

Find two numbers so that the square of the first plus the second, added to the square of the second plus the first equals 238.

SEE ANSWER 130

What is the missing number?

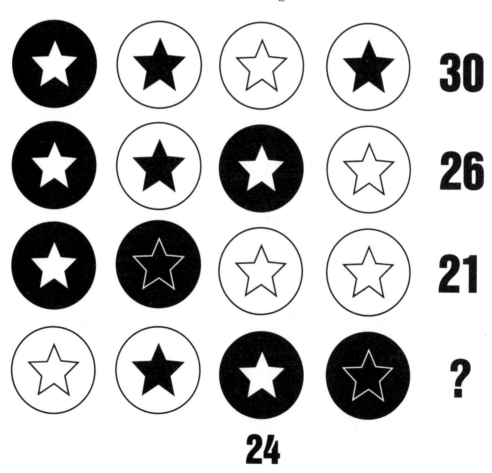

SEE ANSWER 165

Each like symbol has the same value.
Work out the value of the missing digit.

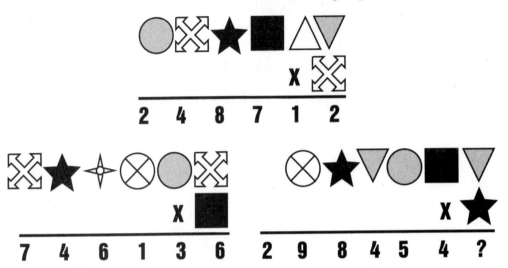

SEE ANSWER 172

PUZZLE 154

Which block of cells fits logically into the space?

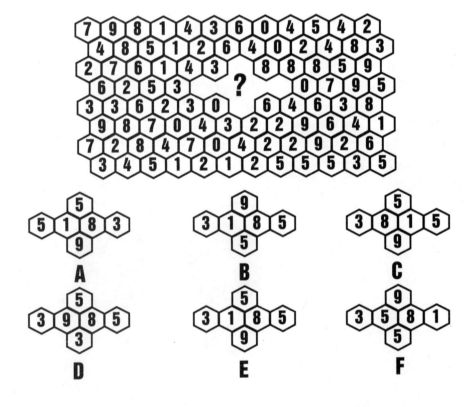

SEE ANSWER 151

A girl asks her mother's age and is told, "Six years ago I was nine times your age. Now I am only three times your age."
What are the present ages of the girl and her mother?

SEE ANSWER 117

How many revolutions per minute does the small wheel make?

? rev / minute

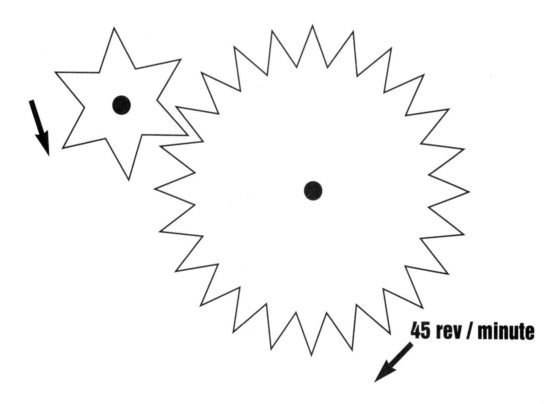

45 rev / minute

SEE ANSWER 178

What is the missing point value?

SEE ANSWER 152

PUZZLE 158

Use three straight lines to divide this square into five sections, each
of which contains a total value of 60.

SEE ANSWER 94

Use logic to find which shape has the greatest perimeter.

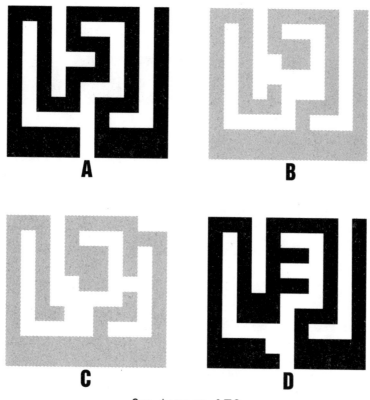

A   B

C   D

SEE ANSWER 179

PUZZLE 160

Supply both the missing numbers.

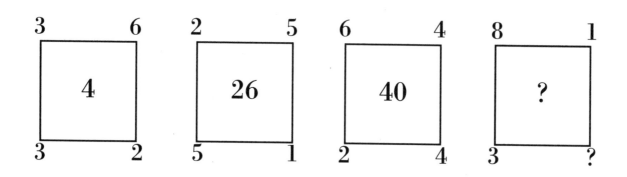

SEE ANSWER 107

PUZZLE 161

Find the block in each row which, when you multiply the highest two numbers together, and add the other two digits in the block to the product to arrive at a solution, then add the solutions from the chosen blocks in the other rows together, will give you the highest possible total. Repeat the process to also find the lowest possible total.

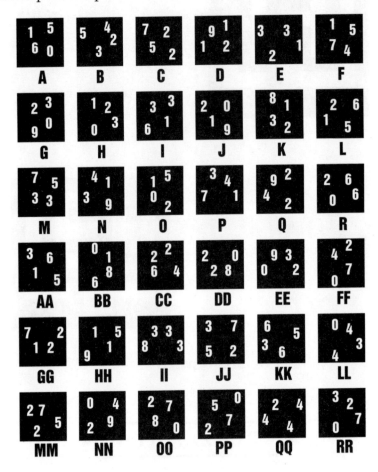

SEE ANSWER 145

PUZZLE 162

What number comes next in the sequence to replace the question mark?

| 2 | 7 | 11 | 20 | 38 | 69 | ? |

SEE ANSWER 118

What number, when you multiply it by three and multiply the result by seven and then add both of the resultant digits, and multiply the result of that by itself, when you add nineteen, gives a number that is a perfect square which can be divided exactly by only seven smaller numbers (excluding one), two of which are prime and two of which are perfect squares?

SEE ANSWER 100

Find hidden within the stars, a long multiplication sum with a six-figure result.

SEE ANSWER 131

Make an exact quarter using all these numbers, and no other.

2 5 2 5 2 5 2 5 0

SEE ANSWER 166

The values represented by the black segments surrounding each number, are processed in two stages to get the numbers in the middle of each system. Find the missing number.

SEE ANSWER 173

Find the missing number.

8   2   3   1   8   4
9   2   3   2   0   ?

SEE ANSWER 157

PUZZLE 168

Which number replaces the question mark?

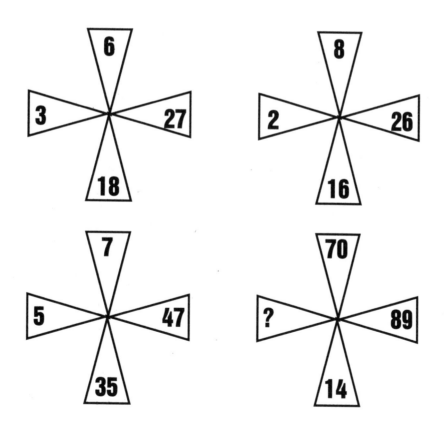

SEE ANSWER 132

PUZZLE 169

What is the missing profit figure?

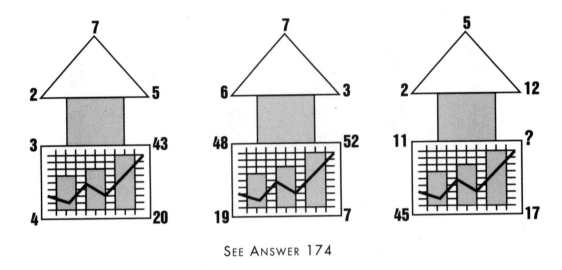

SEE ANSWER 174

PUZZLE 170

Fill the numbers into the blank spaces. There is only one correct way.

ACROSS

30	326	649	2768259
74	359	659	4346540
87	386	691	5783968
93	390	697	6281307
018	467	721	6445535
042	496	735	6490916
133	516	918	6906308
148	519	929	7590936
273	563	954	9473460
298	619	989	9798259
306			

DOWN

043	928	2369674	7533652
192	165263	3268959	7934895
313	320469	4906736	9219367
333	372108	5176453	9452695
344	697469	5364749	9497059
460	0840396	6089148	9687097
521	0929969	7485571	9759968
863			

SEE ANSWER 153

Discover the vital relationship between all of these numbers to find the missing number.

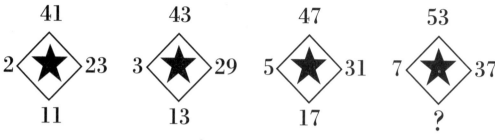

41
2 ⟨★⟩ 23
11

43
3 ⟨★⟩ 29
13

47
5 ⟨★⟩ 31
17

53
7 ⟨★⟩ 37
?

SEE ANSWER 119

What is the value of the target on the right?

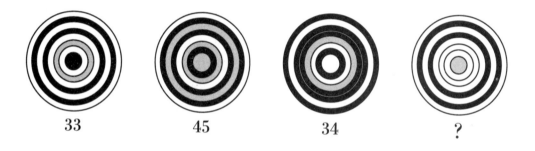

33   45   34   ?

SEE ANSWER 181

A perfect number is a number that is equal to the sum of its factors, excluding itself. The first is 6 (1 + 2 + 3). The next is 28 (1 + 2 + 4 + 7 + 14). The third perfect number falls somewhere between 350 and 550. What is it?

SEE ANSWER 180

This system is balanced. How heavy is the black box (ignoring leverage effects)?

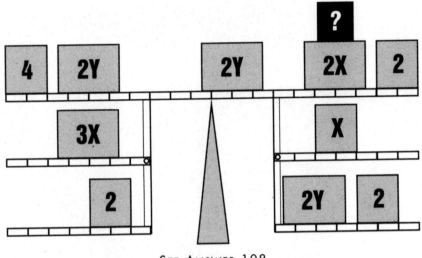

SEE ANSWER 108

PUZZLE 175

Put numbers in the squares above and below each diamond and multiply them together. Do the same with the numbers to the left and right of each diamond and subtract the lower result from the higher to obtain the middle numbers.

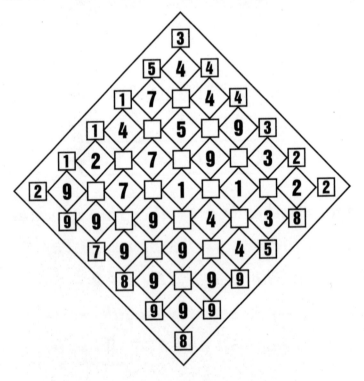

SEE ANSWER 146

If two is added to both the top and bottom of a certain fraction, its value becomes a half. If two is subtracted from both the top and bottom of that same fraction, its value becomes a third. What is the fraction?

SEE ANSWER 95

PUZZLE 177

What is the missing value of this logic series?

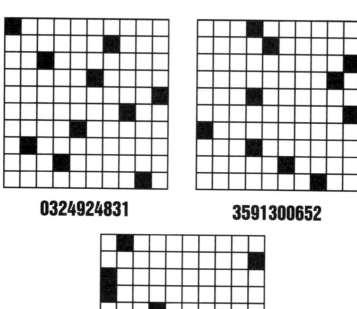

0324924831   **3591300652**

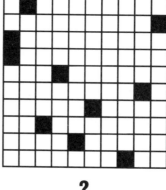

?

SEE ANSWER 101

Complete the analogy.

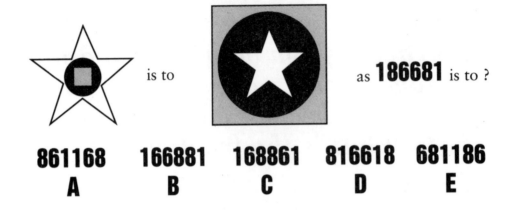

861168	**166881**	**168861**	**816618**	**681186**
A	**B**	**C**	**D**	**E**

SEE ANSWER 137

PUZZLE 179

Working 8-hour days, a kit glider can be built by 7 enthusiasts in a certain number of days. If 7 more enthusiasts helped with the construction of the glider, the work could be completed 7 days sooner, but if there were only 4 enthusiasts, the kit would take 24½ days to complete.
How long would it take 10 enthusiasts to complete the kit in working days, hours and minutes?

SEE ANSWER 96

Which Petri dish of bacteria cultures should replace the question mark?

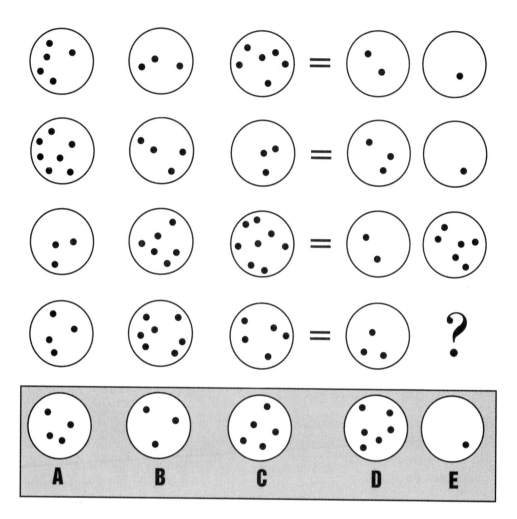

SEE ANSWER 102

When you add two numbers their total is 101. When you compare the numbers, their difference is 27. What are the numbers?

SEE ANSWER 133

Insert the middle numbers.

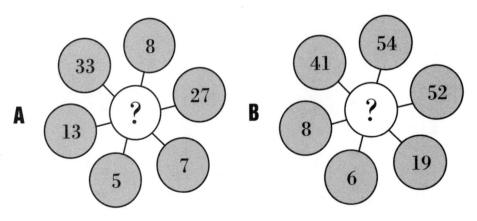

A   B

SEE ANSWER 158

PUZZLE 183

A rectangular plot of land is 28 paces shorter on one side than on the other. If the longer side were reduced by 34 paces, and the smaller side were lengthened by 40 paces, the area contained within the plot would be unchanged. What are the lengths of the sides?

SEE ANSWER 175

PUZZLE 184

What is the missing number in this sequence?

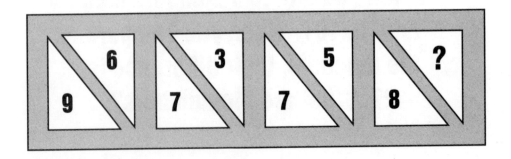

SEE ANSWER 154

PUZZLE 185

Insert the rows into the appropriate places in the grid to make all lines, columns, and long diagonals add to 105.

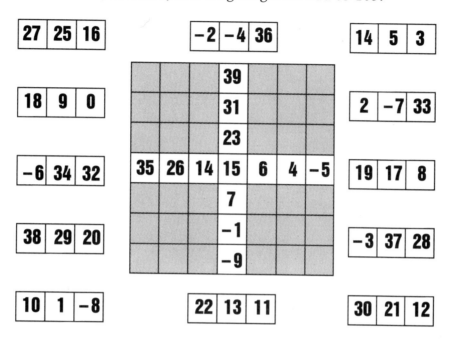

SEE ANSWER 120

PUZZLE 186

What weight balances the pulley system on the right?

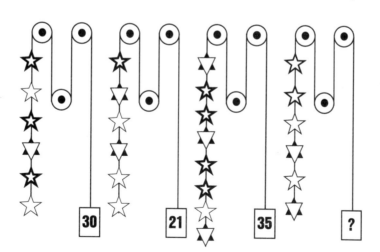

SEE ANSWER 109

1

22	21	13	5	46	38	30
31	23	15	14	6	47	39
40	32	24	16	8	7	48
49	41	33	25	17	9	1
2	43	42	34	26	18	10
11	3	44	36	35	27	19
20	12	4	45	37	29	28

2 96. $4^2 = 16$; $16 \times 6 = 96$

3 32.
Diamond = 7
Circle = 4
Hexagon = 13
Square = 8

4 A. 54, B. 42. Opposite numbers are multiplied, divided, or added to get the numbers in the middle.

5 Thursday. 1952 was a leap year with 366 days. $366 \div 7$ (days in a week) = 52 remainder 2. Tuesday + 2 days = Thursday.

6 5 (4 big and 1 little).

7

	2	9		0	4	8		7	4	6		4	7
4	5	9		4	7	7		4	1	6		1	4	2
2	0	0	8	7	3	2		1	0	5	2	1	5	1
0		5		4		4	7	3		6		2		9
4	8	8		5	6	3		3	1	4		3	8	9
1	4	6	9	4	5	1		1	2	8	5	4	6	5
7	7	5		2	8	5	7	3	7	5		0	1	2
	5			4		7		4			4
1	9	2		2	4	5	7	1	4	9		3	4	5
5	4	1	8	4	0	9		9	5	8	8	8	5	9
8	1	9		4	4	8		4	8	5		5	1	0
4		3		3		4	0	9		5		4		5
5	1	2	5	7	2	1		1	7	9	3	1	7
3	9	4		4	3	7		5	5	0		4	3	9
	8	1		0	1	8		9	0	7		5	9

8 78. Multiply opposite numbers and add the results to get the numbers in the middle. Thus 24 + 24 + 30 = 78.

9 200 Credits. $9 \times 25 - (4 \times 6.25) = 200$.

10

Stars (row 1): 7, 5, 6, 3, 1, 2
(row 2): 3, 7, 8, 1, 5, 6
(row 3): 1, 8, 9, 0, 7, 8
(row 4): 0, 9, 4, 5, 3, 9

11 38 seconds after 8.43.

12 88. $88 + 880 + (4 \times 8) = 1000$.

13 18.
Elephant = 2
Walrus = 3
Camel = 4
Pig = 5

14 7162 and 3581.

15 Follow this route.

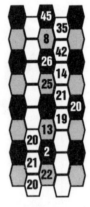

16 7. Take the middle number from the top left number. Multiply that by 2 to get the top right number. Add 5 to the top right number to get the bottom number.

17 D. The the binary numbers start at the top and work left to right, line by line.

1	1	0	1	1	1	0	0	1	0	1
1	1	0	1	1	1	1	0	0	0	1
0	0	1	1	0	1	0	1	0	1	1
1	1	0	0	1	1	0	1	1	1	1
0	1	1	1	1	1	0	0	0	0	1
0	0	0	1	1	0	0	1	0	1	0
0	1	1	0	1	0	0	1	0	1	
0	1	1	0	1	1	0	1	0	1	1
1	1	1	0	0	0	1	1	0	0	1

18 20 July 1969. It was the date of the first manned lunar landing.

19 19. The top pair of numbers are multiplied together and added to the result of multiplying the bottom pair of numbers together. (2 x 8) + (3 x 1).

20 19. They denote the alphanumeric positions of numbers from 1 to 6. The first letter of six is "s", the 19th letter of the alphabet.

21

6	2	9	3	7
3	7	6	2	9
2	9	3	7	6
7	6	2	9	3
9	3	7	6	2

22 6. Add the value of the top two stars of each column to value of the middle two stars to get the value of the bottom two stars.

23 30 x 15 units (the pool's area becomes 18 x 25 units, or 450 square units).

24 2. The weight is positioned 8 units along, so it needs a weight of 2 units (8 x 2 = 16) to keep the system in balance.

25 9 minutes and 9 seconds after 1.

26 A.
Circle = 1
Diamond = 4
Square = 3
Triangle = 2
Hexagon = 5

27 7 people.

28 10.
Snowflake = 5
Candle = 3
Sun = 2

29 D. The paper would reach 3,355.4432 m, which is as high as a mountain.

30 C.
White = 7
Black = 5
Shaded = 3

31 7. There are 7 areas of intersection at this position.

32 28. Each row is a sequence of A + D = C, D + C = B and B + C = E.

33 25.
Circle = 4
Triangle = 8
Diamond = 5
Square = 2
The values are added when the shapes are combined.

34 10 m. The ratio of the flagpole to its shadow is the same as the ratio of the measuring stick to its shadow.

35 11954.
(45911 – 11954 = 33957)

36 3. There are two sequences in the series: 6 x 8 = 48, and 7 x 9 = 63.

37 46 points, taking this route:

9	4	5	3	6	1	8	2
8	1	2	2	3	2	5	1
6	9	9	1	2	4	3	5
4	8	1	3	5	2	6	1
1	4	3	7	6	3	1	4
9	2	4	8	6	4	5	3
4	2	9	4	8	6	7	1
2	8	1	6	5	9	0	1

38 27. The bottom two digits expressed as a number, subtracted from the top two digits, also expressed as a number. The difference is halved and the result is put in the middle. 78 – 24 = 54. 54 ÷ 2 = 27.

39 19.
Shaded = 9
Black = 5
White = 3

40 42. The bottom number goes next to the top one to make a two-digit number; the left and right do the same. Then subtract the second number from the first.
96 – 54 = 42.

41 6. The right weight is nine units across to balance the left three units across. 6 x 9 (54) balances 18 x 3 (54).

42 194. $(1 \times 5^3) + (2 \times 5^2) + (3 \times 5^1) + (4 \times 5^0)$.

43 103.5

44 A. 24. Opposite numbers are divided or added to give 24.
B. 3. Opposite numbers are multiplied or divided by 3.

45 12½ turns. For every unit that the rollers cover, the beam is pushed two units.

46 77 square units.

47 There are 5 cards missing, leaving 47 in the deck.

48 1. The number is an anagram of Mensa, with numbers substituted for the letters.

49 D. The least number of faces touching each other gives the greatest perimeter.

50 16.

51 36.

```
 912        921
x 36       x 36
─────      ─────
5472       5526
2736       2763
─────      ─────
32832      33156
```

52

	25			49		
		26	10			
		27				
	44	28				
	5		29			

53   2. C = A – B, with the result reversed. 496324 – 235768 = 260556.

54   24. The pieces have the following values:

☆ = 5

▽ = 4

☆ = 3

55   E, G, G. These represent the numbers 577, which are added to the sum of the previous top and middle line, to get the bottom line.

56   0. The top two numbers are multiplied in shapes 1, 3 and 5. The answers are put as single-digit numbers in the top triangles of shapes 2, 4 and 6. In all the shapes the top two numbers are multiplied, then halved, 3 x 0 = 0.

57

3	1	8	4		9	1	6		5	1	1	9
5			9	1	5		2	0	0			6
3	0	5	2		1	1	8		8	8	8	5
6		6	0	7	3		1	0	6	6		8
3		6			8		7			5		5
7	1	7	6						2	9	8	3
	1		7	4	2	4	3	6	1		9	
1	6	6	5	9		7		3	5	6	7	7
	7		8		1	5	5		8		5	
5	6	1	5	1		6		5	1	7	1	9
	5		6	0	3	6	3	0	0		1	
2		6		8		2		7		3		2
2	7	7		7	6	8	9	1		7	2	4
9		5	0	5	6		0	3	6	0		8
1	0	4	8					9	4	8		1
3		4		7		8			0			4
7		5	8	3	2		7	7	5			3
1	9	1	8		6	5	3		9	8	5	7
5			9	5	1		3	9	0			7
2	3	9	0		2	9	3		0	1	9	3

58

59   2. The top four numbers, plus the number in the middle, equals the bottom four numbers. Hence 8765 + 567 = 9332.

60

6	8	0	9	4	1	**6**	4	1	6	2	2	2
3	4	5	6	3	4	**1**	2	1	9	1	8	3
6	2	1	6	1	4	**4**	4	3	2	7	0	8
9	2	2	8	4	6	**1**	5	2	9	5	5	0
0	1	6	2	1	9	**3**	2	0	0	0	2	5
2	8	1	2	1	2	**1**	5	8	5	8	7	1
9	3	9	4	5	0	**4**	6	3	9	5	1	2
3	1	6	1	7	6	**2**	1	1	3	2	6	7
7	9	2	2	8	9	**6**	5	6	1	2	3	1
0	2	2	3	8	4	**0**	4	6	1	2	8	9
8	5	4	0	4	3	**2**	6	1	6	1	4	2
5	2	6	1	6	0	**9**	3	4	1	7	2	8

61 Carlos is oldest; Maccio is youngest. (From oldest to youngest: Carlos, Juan, Za-za, Fifi, Jorjio, Maccio.)

62 12, 19, 26, 3, 10. The bottom line of a Magic Square, in which all rows, columns, and long diagonals equal 70.

63 72. It is the only non-square number.

64

3		5		4		4		3		3
	90		120		64		144		54	
2		3		2		2		6		1
	48		96		16		72		36	
1		8		2		2		3		2
	160		80		20		150		30	
4		5		1		5		5		1
	180		10		40		100		15	
9		1		2		4		1		3
	27		8		32		12		81	
3		1		4		1		3		9
	24		28		84		45		135	
8		1		7		3		5		1
	144		42		63		225		25	
3		6		1		3		5		1

65 24 ways. There are six alternatives with each suit at the left.

66 21 times.

67 15:03 (or 03.15 (pm) if the watch has the capacity to switch to 12-hour mode).

68 8 earth months. Zero has an orbit that takes $\sqrt{4^3}$ (8) times as long as Hot.

69 10 people.

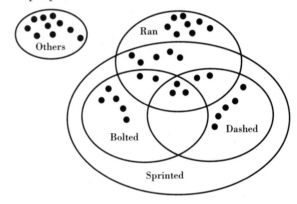

70 1. A + B = KL, C + D = MN, and so on.

71 A = 5. (a + b) – (d + e) = c
B = 0. (d + e) – (a + b) = c
C = 3. a + b + c – e = d
D = 2. c + d + e – a = b

72 Five men. Each man digs 1 hole in 5 hours, and thus 20 holes in 100 hours.

73 4. Start from the top left of the spiral and work in, successively subtracting and adding: 9 – 7 = 2, 2 + 5 = 7, etc.

74 22.
Rectangle = 8
Triangle = 3
Hexagon = 2

75 D. This is the only patch that works for all the lines.

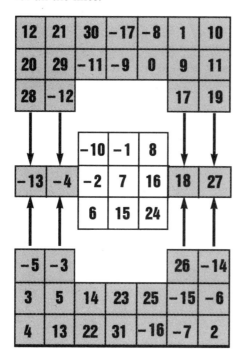

76 400. The numbers are the squares of 14 to 21 inclusive.

77 248. Long lines = 2, short lines = 1. Add the values on the right to arrive at the answer.

78 1258 x 6874.

79 B. Each nodule is given a value, depending on its position in the grid. The values are added together.

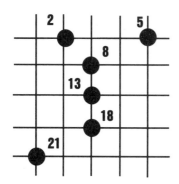

80 279. The numbers are added together and the sum + 1 is put in the next triangle. 106 + 172 = 278 + 1 + 279

81 B. The shaded spots represent the hands of a clock. 3:00 – 9:00 = 6:00.

82 25. Star = 9, Whorl = 5, Square = 3

83 34. Write the alphabet in a 3-row grid with the following values: A, J, S = 1; B, K, T = 2; C, L, U = 3; D, M, V = 4; E, N, W = 5; F, O, X = 6; G, P, Y = 7; H, Q, Z = 8; I, R = 9. Thus, Raphael = 9 + 1 + 7 + 8 + 1 + 5 + 3 = 34.

84 Any number. This amazing formula will always end up with the number you first thought of, with 00 at the end.

85 3. Add the spots and take the middle line from the top line.

86 3 units. The difference of 24 divided by 8.

87 P = 19. Map the alphabet into 2 rows of 13 each. Then add the numerical values of each row to get the value of the letters. A (1) + N (14) = 15. P comes two letters after N in the alphabet, so add two to the top and two to the bottom (16 + 3 = 19).

88 C. The 1st and 2nd numbers in each line, multiplied together, equal the last two numbers. The 3rd and 4th numbers multiplied together, equal the 6th and 7th. The 6th and 7th numbers minus the 8th and 9th numbers equal the 5th number of each line.

89 14. Divide the left number by 3 and add 4 to give the middle number. Repeat the sums with the middle number to get the right number. 78 ÷ 3 = 26; 26 + 4 = 30; 30 ÷ 3 = 10; 10 + 4 = 14.

90

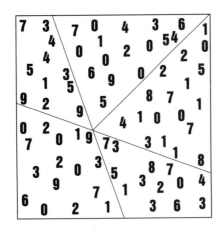

91 7. In each box, top left x bottom right = bottom left and top right. The products are a two-digit number reading up.

92 8. In each box the top two dishes expressed as numbers are multiplied to give the middle two dishes. The middle two dishes are then multiplied in the same way to give the bottom two.
6 x 4 = 24; 2 x 4 = 8.

93 32 hours. The hole will have eight times the volume. It would take 12 men eight times as long to dig it, and 16 times as long for 6 men.

94

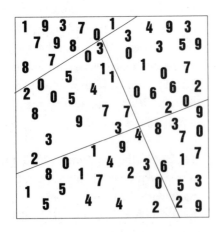

95 $\frac{6}{14}$

96 9 working days, 6 hours, 24 minutes. As it takes 4 enthusiasts 24.5 days (196 hours) to build the gilder, it would take 1 person 98 days (784 hours) and 10 people 9.8 days (78.4 hours) to complete the job. Each 0.1 of an hour is 6 minutes.

97 3. Reverse the second line and subtract it from the top line to get the bottom line. 43390 – 25587 = 17803.

98 Black hexagon = 2
White hexagon = 4
Shaded hexagon = 7

99

```
5 5 9 3 3 1 2 1 7 9 8 5 2 7 9
5 2 1 7 3 8 5 1 2 8 5 3 5 0 6
1 7 1 8 1 4 3 9 5 6 0 1 0 5 0
2 0 3 8 9 2 8 7 1 4 2 9 2 0 7
6 1 9 7 1 5 3 9 3 8 4 5 3 6 2
5 2 7 3 6 2 8 1 7 9 8 2 4 9 0
1 7 2 1 8 1 5 2 9 5 3 6 0 7
5 8 1 9 0 3 7 9 0 7 3 4 2 7 5
4 2 7 3 9 8 2 1 3 4 5 1 8 7 0
9 4 5 8 7 2 0 6 7 8 3 0 7 2 2
4 3 9 0 2 4 3 8 2 4 1 7 5 1 0
0 8 1 5 9 8 1 5 6 7 9 6 3 8 7
9 5 3 4 7 3 9 2 9 4 1 8 1 9 7
0 2 5 1 7 5 1 8 3 0 5 4 0 3 5
8 1 0 3 8 1 3 0 4 1 3 6 1 7 6
```

100 3. 3 x 3 [9] x 7 [63]; 6 + 3 [9] x 9 [81]; 81 + 19 = 100. 100 is 10^2 and it is divisible by 2 (prime number), 4 (also 2^2), 5 (prime number), 10, 20, 25 (also 5^2) and 50.

101 1009315742. The number of white boxes before the black box on each line, counting alternately from left and right.

102 B. Count the bacteria in each Petri dish, then multiply the first number by the second number and add the third number to the product. The 2-digit result follows. (4 x 7) + 5 = 33.

103 35. White hexagons have no value. Black hexagons are worth 1 in the top row, 2 in the second row, 3 in the third row, 4 in the fourth row, then 3 in the fifth row, 2 in the sixth row and 1 in the seventh row.

104 975310.

105 5. Each line contains three separate multiplication sums with the answer in between the multipliers. 10 ÷ 2 = 5.

106 The sum is 7153 – 6482 = 671. Move the pieces as follows:

1 2 3 4 5 6 7 8

6 7 **1** 2 3 4 5 8

6 7 **1** 2 5 3 **4** 8

6 2 7 1 5 3 **4** 8

6 **4** 8 2 7 1 5 3

107

8   1

| 48 |

3   3

In each box, multiply the two bottom numbers and square the product to get the two top numbers. Read the top and bottom numbers as 2-digit figures and subtract the smaller from the larger.
$\sqrt{81} = 9$; 9 ÷ 3 = 3; 81 – 33 = 48.

108 2 units.

109 24. Pieces have the following values:

☆ = 7

✡ = 1

☆ = 4

110 12345679 (x 63) = 777777777.

111 252.
Black triangle = 6
White triangle = 3
12 x 21 = 252.

112 5. The numbers in all the triangles add up to 49.

113 31.
White ring = 4
Black ring = 6
Shaded ring = 3

114

115 D. The two sections of each shape fit together to form a magic square. Each row of the other three add to 16, but each row of D adds to 19.

116 2. Each row adds to 40.

117 The girl is now 8, and her mother is 24.

118 127. Three adjoining numbers are added together in a continuous string. 20 + 38 + 69 = 127.

119 19. Map the prime numbers from 2 to 53 into four columns.

120

10	1	−8	39	30	21	12
2	−7	33	31	22	13	11
−6	34	32	23	14	5	3
35	26	14	15	6	4	−5
27	25	16	7	−2	−4	36
19	17	8	−1	−3	37	28
18	9	0	−9	38	29	20

121 456. The first symbols are worth 789; the middle symbols are worth 456; the right-hand symbols are worth 123.

122 $9^{(9^9)}$ (nine [to the power of nine, to the power of nine]). Solve the top power first, giving nine to the power of 387420489. The result is a number so large that it has never been calculated.

123 8. The squares are numbered from 1 to 9, starting on the top left, from left to right, right to left, left to right.

124 Small black balls weigh 6 units. White balls weigh 4 units.

125 6 and 3. 6 x 3 = 18; 1 + 8 = 9 (and 6 + 3 = 9); 9 + 9 = 18.

126 121. Each block has a value according to its position in the grid. The blocks are numbered from 1 to 84, starting at the top right, and working right to left, left to right, right to left, etc. The black blocks in each column are then added together.

127 6. In each case, the sum of the numbers outside a hexagon equals the sum of the numbers inside it.

128

$$\frac{6729}{13458}$$

129

8	8	7	6	2	5	5	4	5	4	4	7	0	0	1
1	2	3	1	3	5	0	1	5	7	6	1	2	0	8
6	9	2	5	2	8	1	8	0	2	7	9	5	3	9
8	7	0	9	1	7	2	9	3	5	3	8	9	2	0
1	0	2	6	0	3	9	1	6	7	0	7	1	7	6
9	8	1	5	9	9	5	6	5	0	3	2	9	0	0
3	0	7	2	9	1	8	0	7	7	8	0	7	6	9
7	8	5	3	2	6	0	8	9	2	9	9	1	2	0
2	9	1	7	0	7	7	1	9	7	8	3	0	0	9
1	0	3	2	5	0	5	2	5	1	6	7	2	8	9
6	2	9	0	9	6	0	9	1	3	8	5	0	7	9
9	0	9	8	5	0	3	2	9	1	0	9	9	1	0

130 7 and 13. 7^2 (49) + 13 = 62. 7 + 13^2 (169) = 176. 62 + 176 = 238

131

132 5. The three smallest numbers are added together to give the largest number. The largest number is always on the right.
5 + 14 + 70 = 89.

133 37 and 64.

134

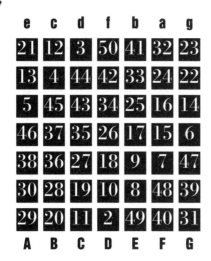

135

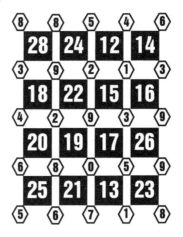

136

137 E. What was external becomes internal, and vice-versa.

138 16 people.

139 142857. The numbers are:
(x 1) 142857
(x 2) 285714
(x 3) 428571
(x 4) 571428
(x 5) 714285
(x 6) 857142

140 2 units. The difference of 16 divided by 8. The units to the right come to 104, to the left they are 86. 104 – 86 = 18. The blank box is 9 units across so 2 x 9 = 18.

141 It was 8 x 5 units. This becomes 10 x 4 units, retaining the area of 40 square units.

142

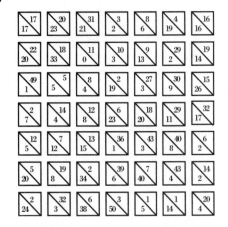

143 The route is:

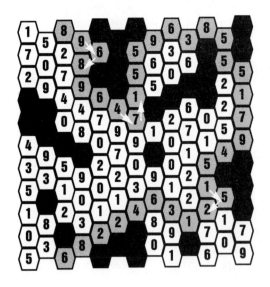

144 73.

145 The highest possible total is 268, using boxes F, L, M, BB, HH, OO. The sums are: (7 x 5) [35] + 4 + 1 = *40*. (6 x 5) [30] + 2 + 1 = *33*. (7 x 5) [35] + 3 + 3 = *41*. (8 x 6) [48] + 1 + 0 = *49*. (9 x 5) [45] + 1 + 1 = *47*. (8 x 7) [56] + 2 + 0 = *58*. 40 + 33 + 41 + 49 + 47 + 58 = 268.

The lowest possible total is 87, using boxes E, H, O, DD, GG, QQ. The sums are: (3 x 3) [9] + 2 + 1 = *12*. (3 x 2) [6] + 1 + 0 = *7*. (5 x 2) [10] + 1 + 0 = *11*. (8 x 2) [16] + 2 + 0 = *18*. (7 x 2) [14] + 2 + 1 = *17*. (4 x 4) [16] + 4 + 2 = *22*. 12 + 7 + 11 + 18 + 17 + 22 = 87.

146

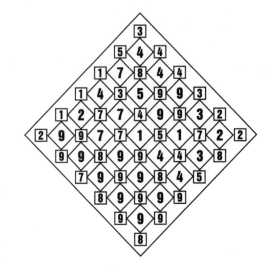

147 See opposite page

148 5. The first three digits expressed as a whole number, subtracted from the next three digits, expressed as a whole number, equals the last three digits. 623 – 188 = 435.

147

[A grid of numbers and stars puzzle answer]

148 5. 623 – 188 = 435.

149 3. Add the left top and bottom numbers together, add the right top and bottom numbers together. Subtract the smaller from the larger to get the middle number. (15 + 5) – (13 + 4) = 3.

150 20.
Long bar = 8
Short bar = 2

151 E. Label each row of cells from the left, and do the following multiplications:
b x k = fg; c x j = eh; a x l = di.

152 1. The sum of the four smallest values equals the largest value. The largest value rotates by one turn clockwise each star.

153

[A grid of numbers and circles puzzle answer]

154 6. The numbers in the left triangles of each pair of split blocks, when multiplied together, equals the numbers in the right-hand triangles of each pair of split blocks. 7 x 8 = 56.

155 Dog = 12
Horse = 9
Cat = 7
Pig = 5

156

Move one place to the right in the alphabet. A = 2, B = 3. The numbers to make espresso are E = 6, S = 20, P = 17, R = 19 and O = 16.

157 7. Each line is a multiplication sum without symbols or spaces.
8 x 23 = 184
9 x 23 = 207

158 A = 40, B = 60. Opposite numbers are multiplied or added to get the numbers in the middle.

159 24.
Elephant = 4
Pig = 2
Camel = 6

160 27. The left number is one-third of the top and the right is subtracted from the top number to give the bottom.

161 17 x 65359477124183 = 1111111111111111.

162 2057, joined by 613, x 6.
The sum is 2057613 x 6 = 12345678.

163 20. In each shape, the values are of the black squares. In column 1, they are worth 2; in column 2, they are worth 4; in column 3, they are worth 6 and in column 4, they are worth 8. The values are added together and the total goes at the bottom.

164 140592. 140592 ÷ 3 = 46864.

165 23. The shapes have the following values:

7   9   5   2

166

$$\frac{5555}{22220}$$

167 4. In each row, the numbers in the two left balloons equal the numbers in the three right balloons.

168 70. Each star is valued from 1 to 9, depending on its position in the columns from the left of each row. The values are then multiplied. The stars appear in columns 1, 2, 5 and 7, so the sums are: 1 x 2 (2) x 5 (10) x 7 = 70.

169

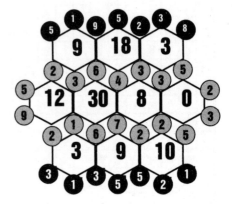

170 21.
Whorl = 5
Checkered box = 13
Star = 3

171 41 offspring.

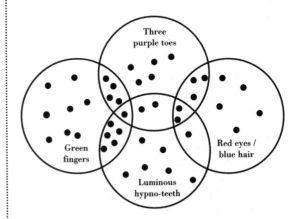

172 4. The sums are
124356 x 2 = 248712
248712 x 3 = 746136
746136 x 4 = 2984544
The shapes have the values above right:

172

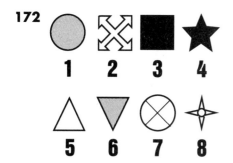

173 5. Use the values represented by the black spots in the puzzle, numbered as below. Multiply each top pair of values together to get the values for the bottom pair, and subtract the bottom left value from the top right value.
4 x 7 = 28; 7 – 2 = 5.

174 47. Add together all the numbers around each graph, bottom. Multiply together the three numbers around the roof, top. The answers should be the same.
5 x 2 x 12 = 120. 47 + 45 + 17 + 11 = 120.

175 68 x 40 paces (becoming 34 x 80 paces). The area remains 2720 paces².

176 100. The numbers inside each triangle total 200.

177 39. Each diamond contains three numbers. To get the bottom number, multiply the left by the middle, and add the product to the sum of the right and the left. (5 x 6) + 5 + 4 = 39.

178 180 revolutions. (45 revolutions x 24 teeth of big wheel [1080 movements]) ÷ 6 (teeth of small wheel) = 180.

179 A. The thinnest shape to cover an area always has the greatest perimeter.

180 496. 1 + 2 + 4 + 8 + 16 + 31 + 62 + 124 + 248 = 496.

181 32.
White ring = 3
Shaded ring = 9
Black ring = 4

182 + 29, x 7, – 94, x 4 and – 435. The sum is: 29 x 7 (203) – 94 (109) x 4 (436) – 435 = 1.

183 30. Multiply the top two numbers together and the bottom two numbers together. Then subtract the lower from the higher and then put answer in the middle. This is done continuously. (12 x 7) [84] – (9 x 6) [54] = 30.

184 425. Reverse the top line, subtract the second line from that, and subtract the result from the bottom line to get the three figure sum for the blanks. 6130 – 2589 = 3541; 3966 – 3541 = 425.

185 B. The values of the shapes are:

 = 5

 = 2

 = 6

 = 4

 = 3

186 27.

Shaded hexagon / white star = 3
Black hexagon / shaded star = 5
White hexagon / black star = 8

WORD PUZZLES

The world's fascination with word puzzles is almost as old as civilization. Riddles that everyone knows today, like the old chestnut, "As I was going to St. Ives I met a man with seven wives… " have exact equivalents in the Babylonia of Biblical times. Today, when so many traditional pastimes seem to have been superseded by more exciting games spiced with modern technology, word puzzles are more popular than ever.

Mensa's puzzle books have in many ways become victims of their own success. Our early efforts sold so widely that now each new book has to be written with an eye to foreign markets. We not only have to cope with the differences between British and American English, but with the need for the books to be readily translatable into a wide variety of other languages. We are proud to have editions not only in French and German but in less widely spoken languages such as Finnish and Afrikaans.

Working under such constraints has pushed us to heights of ingenuity and creativity which we little dreamt of when the series began. This book is the work of my colleagues Carolyn Skitt and Bobby Raikhy. Carolyn is the powerhouse of British Mensa's puzzle writing department. Her work appears in countless newspapers and magazines. Though you may not recognize her name you will probably have tried her puzzles before. And Bobby is responsible for the technical side, getting Carolyn's ideas onto the computer. As usual, puzzles have been checked by the ever-keen David Ballheimer, whose enthusiasm knows no bounds.

This international outlook exactly matches the world view of Mensa itself. We have well over 100,000 members in countries throughout the world. They enjoy a social club that is unique. There is only one criterion for entering Mensa and that is the ability to pass an intelligence test within the top two percent. The members meet for social and intellectual stimulation and soon find themselves part of a true "intelligence network" which spans the globe. What is more, with the advent of the internet, they find contact with other Mensans throughout the world has never been easier.

If you would like to join Mensa, joining details are in the Introduction at the start of this book.

R. P. Allen

Robert Allen
Editorial Director
Mensa Publications

Can you work out what letter needs to be inserted in the middle to form four dances by combining opposite segments?

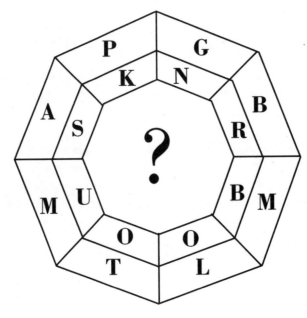

SEE ANSWER 122

Move from square to touching square – including diagonals – to discover the name of a city.

P	H	N	G
C	E	A	G
P	O	E	N

SEE ANSWER 9

PUZZLE 3

At an exhibition there are 207 Calvin Klein creations, 512 outfits by Vivienne Westwood and 100 Jasper Conran outfits. How many items by Giorgio Armani are there at the exhibition?

SEE ANSWER 17

PUZZLE 4

The names of the following ten chefs can be found in this grid on either vertical, horizontal or diagonal lines. Can you find them?

Raymond Blanc

Paul Bocuse

Robert Carrier

Keith Floyd

Rosamund Grant

Ken Hom

Bruno Loubet

Gary Rhodes

Albert Roux

Anthony Tobin

T	N	A	R	G	D	N	U	M	A	S	O	R
B	Y	N	L	K	L	Q	O	X	C	B	O	A
Q	W	T	F	Z	P	H	K	U	J	B	G	Y
Y	G	H	V	S	N	X	E	O	E	R	C	M
D	V	O	W	E	M	D	I	R	S	U	K	O
J	K	N	K	D	B	P	T	T	U	N	O	N
P	M	Y	S	O	S	C	H	R	C	O	P	D
P	F	T	Y	H	A	Y	F	E	O	L	J	B
Z	W	O	U	R	Z	G	L	B	B	O	C	L
F	C	B	R	Y	Q	K	O	L	L	U	F	A
Y	V	I	D	R	J	F	Y	A	U	B	R	N
W	E	N	V	A	Y	Q	D	P	A	E	W	C
R	G	K	P	G	R	Z	B	Y	P	T	P	Q

SEE ANSWER 27

By taking a segment and finding its pair the names of four books from the Old Testament can be made. What are they?

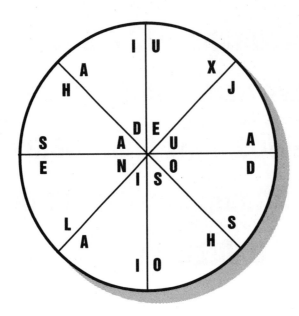

SEE ANSWER 37

In the china department of a large store there are 90 items of Wedgewood, 120 items of Royal Doulton and 140 items of Royal Worcester. How many items of Spode are there?

SEE ANSWER 43

The vowels have been missed out of the following groups of letters.
Replace the vowels and rearrange each group to form the
name of a city. What are the four cities?

STPDB

DNNL

KHLCSTM

RMDD

SEE ANSWER 52

PUZZLE 8

The family names of three athletes have been merged together here.
Who are they?

K	N	E	L	S	L
N					E
H		G	B		O
C			J		L
N	O	A	U		Y
					N

SEE ANSWER 61

Rearrange each of the following groups of letters to form a place in the United States. Which is the odd one out?

AILFORD

ALEEWARD

ORKNYBOL

OZARNIA

SEE ANSWER 58

If the code for Monica Seles is **GIHCWU MYFYM**
who are these other famous tennis stars?

(i) JUN WUMB

(ii) MNYZZC ALUZ

(iii) UHXLY UAUMMC

(iv) GULNCHU HUPLUNCFIPU

(v) WIHWBCNU GULNCHYT

SEE ANSWER 66

PUZZLE 11

2B	5D	4A		3A	1D	1B	4E	5E	1A
1E	3E	2E		2C	5B	4C	3B	1C	2D

The wordframe above, when filled with the correct letters, will give the name of a pop singer. The letters are arranged in the grid below.

There are two possible alternatives to fill each square of the wordframe, one correct, the other incorrect. Who is the singer?

	A	B	C	D	E
1	Y	R	V	N	B
2	P	F	M	Q	G
3	J	L	Y	W	O
4	B	U	K	C	S
5	D	A	T	H	E

SEE ANSWER 75

PUZZLE 12

Two letters are missing from each of the following anagrams of famous people. Can you spot what letters are missing (maybe more than once) and how the people are connected?

TWE – – –   YGU – –   DESI – –   TGRE – – –

SEE ANSWER 81

123

In a car race six cars are lined up behind each other. No. 12 is two places in front of No. 3 who is two places in front of No. 21. No. 7 is behind both No. 11 and No. 3 but in front of No. 21. No. 8 is in front of No. 21 but behind No. 11. What is the finishing order of the cars if car No. 21 moves forward two positions, car No. 8 moves back 3 places, car No. 3 moves forward two places, car No. 11 moves back two places and car No. 12 moves forward one place?

SEE ANSWER 93

Can you work out what letter needs to be inserted in the middle to form four famous composers by combining opposite segments?

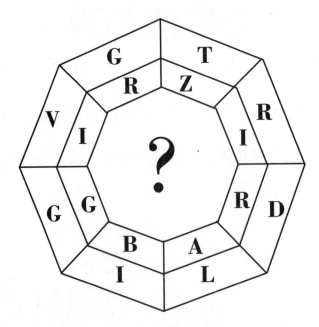

SEE ANSWER 119

What is the next letter in this sequence?

C H L O ?

SEE ANSWER 84

PUZZLE 16

Adam drinks Advocaat and he drives a Datsun. He has a collection of albums by Annie Lennox. Does Adam fly with Virgin or Monarch airline?

SEE ANSWER 98

Four connected names are concealed here. What are they?

WEISSHORN
CHINA
CHANEL
TANGANYKA

SEE ANSWER 108

Rearrange these four American states in the grid provided so that
a European currency can be read down the shaded boxes:

Arkansas, Maryland, Illinois and Michigan.

What is the currency?

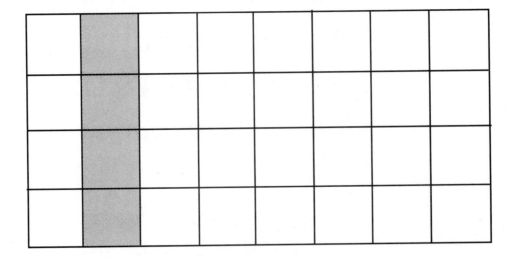

SEE ANSWER 110

Complete the square with the letters of P A R I S. When completed
no row, column or diagonal line will contain the same letter more
than once. One horizontal line will spell the word correctly.
What letter should replace the question mark?

P	A	R		
			?	
		S	P	

SEE ANSWER 126

Collect one letter from each segment to give the name of an
American state. What is it?

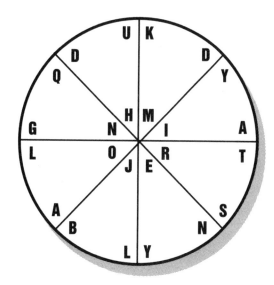

SEE ANSWER 134

PUZZLE 21

What letter is missing from the end turret?
Clue: Actors

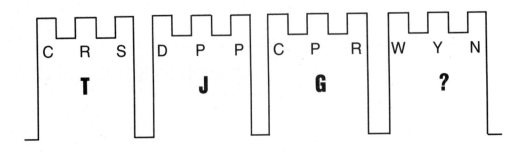

SEE ANSWER 140

PUZZLE 22

Two sides of this pyramid can be seen, but the other two are obscured. Two eight-letter country names are written round the pyramid. What are they?

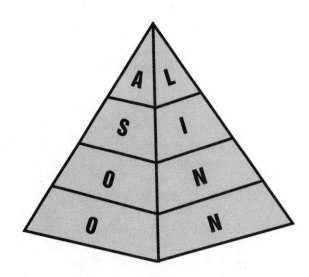

SEE ANSWER 145

A knight, which moves either one square horizontally and two vertically or two horizontally and one vertically, is positioned on this unusual chess board on position A1. Move to each square once in the correct sequence to find the names of four famous scientists.

	1	2	3	4	5
A	C	I	I	N	L
B	O	L	E	N	N
C	E	E	N	S	E
D	L	T	U	S	B
E	S	T	E	W	I

SEE ANSWER 150

This is an unusual maze. Find four separate routes through the maze without any route crossing another, although they may share the same path. On each route collect 7 letters only to give you the names of four books in the Old Testament.

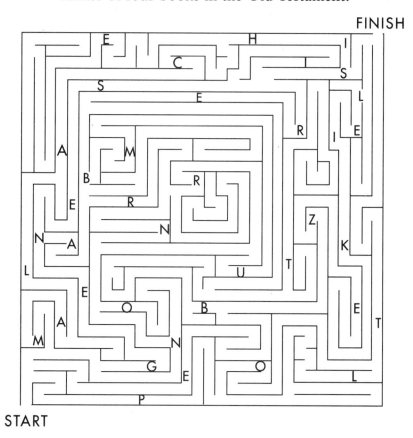

FINISH

START

SEE ANSWER 156

In a horse race Sawgrass came second and Sea Dancer came fourth.

Where did Sky Trap and Noble Romance finish?

SEE ANSWER 162

PUZZLE 26

Some letters have been omitted from this alphabet.
Use the missing letters to form the name of a car manufacturer.

W K C Y D Z I B H
G X P F
M O J S V Q

SEE ANSWER 2

PUZZLE 27

Move from square to touching square – including diagonals – to discover the name of a composer.

H	C	T	S
I	A	V	K
K	O	Y	Z

SEE ANSWER 10

PUZZLE 28

At a European garage there are:
5 Rovers,
115 Vauxhalls
and 50 Renaults.
How many Suzukis
are there?

SEE ANSWER 18

The vowels have been missed out of the following groups of letters.
Replace the vowels and rearrange each group to form the name of
an American state. What are the four states?

SYNPLVNN

SSMTSTSCH

CTTCCNN

NMNTS

SEE ANSWER 53

The names of the following ten champagnes can be found in this
grid on vertical, horizontal and diagonal lines. Can you find them?

Ayala
Bollinger
De Venoge
Deutz
Gosset
Henriot
Lanson
Pol Roger
Ruinart
Salon

D	G	J	B	F	H	C	L	G	B
D	E	U	T	Z	E	A	A	O	M
C	T	V	H	W	N	P	L	S	F
P	R	V	E	S	R	L	A	S	H
S	A	L	O	N	I	Q	Y	E	K
K	N	N	J	N	O	X	A	T	D
B	I	W	G	V	T	G	Q	B	W
D	U	E	Z	K	F	X	E	Y	G
F	R	E	G	O	R	L	O	P	Y
Q	G	X	V	C	H	X	Z	O	D

SEE ANSWER 28

By taking a segment and finding its pair the names of four tennis stars can be found. Who are they?

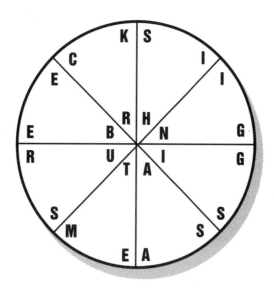

SEE ANSWER 38

PUZZLE 32

Certain pop stars are going on tour over the next few months. Meat Loaf has 6 gigs arranged, Gloria Estefan has 14 gigs organized and George Michael has 12 gigs arranged. How many Bon Jovi gigs will there be?

SEE ANSWER 44

Rearrange each of the following groups of letters to read the names of four famous people. Which name is the odd one out?

HIDMARCSEE

GOALLIE

NINESITE

BIGLESREP

SEE ANSWER 59

PUZZLE 34

These anagrams of famous pop stars surnames have had two letters removed from them. Can you name the stars and what letters have been removed (maybe more than once)?

LLCIS – –

EL – – – –

SEJ – –

DDMAI – –

KACJS – –

SEE ANSWER 82

The names of three film stars have been merged together here.
Who are they?

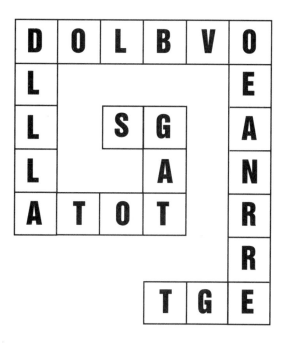

SEE ANSWER 62

PUZZLE 36

If the name WOODROW WILSON is

⊘ ⊕ ⊕ ⊗ ⊖ ⊕ ⊘   ⊘ ⊘ ⊙ ⊗ ⊕ ⊝

Who are the other U.S. Presidents?

⊘ ⊘ ⊙ ⊙   ⊘ ⊝ ⊘ ⊝ ⊗ ⊕ ⊝

⊝ ⊘ ⊖ ⊝ ⊖ ⊘ ⊝   ⊙ ⊘ ⊝ ⊘ ⊕ ⊙ ⊝

⊘ ⊗ ⊕ ⊖ ⊘ ⊗   ⊘ ⊘ ⊗ ⊖ ⊝ ⊘ ⊘ ⊗ ⊕ ⊝

⊖ ⊘ ⊖ ⊖ ⊘   ⊗   ⊘ ⊖ ⊘ ⊝ ⊘ ⊝

⊘ ⊕ ⊖ ⊝   ⊕   ⊘ ⊗ ⊝ ⊘ ⊗ ⊗ ⊘

⊘ ⊙ ⊝ ⊗ ⊗ ⊗ ⊗   ⊘ ⊝ ⊘ ⊝ ⊗

SEE ANSWER 67

1E	4A	3C	3A	1D	5C	3D		4D	1D	4C	1A	4E
							▓▓▓▓					
5C	1C	2B	2D	4B	2E	5B		1A	5E	2E	3B	2C

The wordframe above, when filled with the correct letters, will give
the name of a tennis player. The letters are arranged in the grid
below. There are two possible alternatives to fill each square of the
wordframe, one correct, the other incorrect.

Who is the tennis player?

	A	B	C	D	E
1	N	W	I	O	M
2	R	C	G	D	A
3	H	F	Y	L	V
4	S	A	L	C	E
5	T	K	E	P	H

SEE ANSWER 76

What are the next two letters in this sequence?

B D G I M O ? ?

SEE ANSWER 85

Looking at one side of a bus with two rows of single seats you can see four seats upstairs and four downstairs. Mrs Davis is sitting two seats behind Mr Evans. Mrs Graves is sitting above Mrs Bates and Mr Adams is sitting above Mr Connors. Mr Evans sits above Mrs Harris at the front of the bus. Mr Connors is sitting three seats behind Mrs Harris. Mrs Davis sits on the top deck and Mr Francis sits behind Mrs Bates on the lower deck. Who is sitting where?

SEE ANSWER 94

PUZZLE 40

Laura wears Chanel clothes and her perfume is Oscar de la Renta. Her favourite sculptor is Jules Dalou and she likes Royal Worcester for her dinner service. Is Laura's favourite tennis player Martina Navratilova or Steffi Graf?

SEE ANSWER 99

If the name of a book from the Old Testament is placed with each of the following groups of letters, each group can be rearranged to give the name of a pop singer or pop group. Who are they?

(i) HNONNN
(ii) VONI
(iii) LONIYET

SEE ANSWER 109

PUZZLE 42

Rearrange the order of these six famous actors' second names to give the name of another famous actor in the shaded diagonal line.

Steve MARTIN, Andy GARCIA, Gary COOPER, Eddie MURPHY, Keanu REAVES, Lee MARVIN.

Who is the actor given in the diagonal?

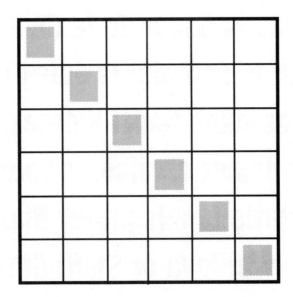

SEE ANSWER 111

Can you work out what letter needs to be inserted in the middle to form four capital cities by combining opposite segments?

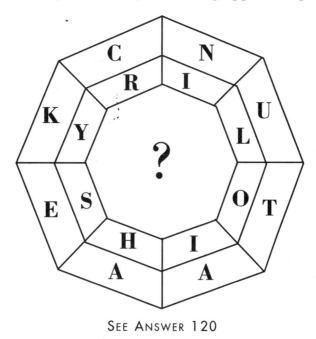

SEE ANSWER 120

Complete the square with the letters of I D A H O. When completed no row, column or diagonal line will contain the same letter more than once. One horizontal line will spell the word correctly. What letter should replace the question mark?

?				
	A	H	O	
	O	I		

SEE ANSWER 127

Take one letter from each segment to find
the name of a Canadian city. What is it?

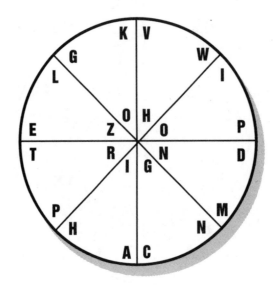

SEE ANSWER 135

PUZZLE 46

What letters are missing from the end boxes?

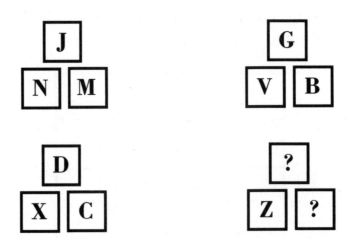

SEE ANSWER 141

Two sides of this pyramid, on a triangular base, can be seen the other one is obscured. Two six-letter composers' names are written round the figure. Who are they?

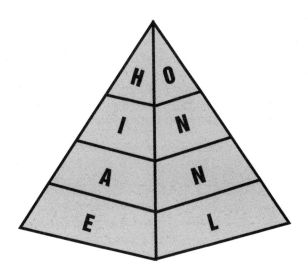

SEE ANSWER 146

A knight, which moves either one square horizontally and two vertically or two horizontally and one vertically, starts at the shaded square of this small chess board visiting each square without returning to the same square twice. Find the route which spells out four famous cartoon characters.

I	R	P	I	O
B	C	G	E	A
E	L		Y	B
I	A	T	L	D
U	L	N	M	O

SEE ANSWER 151

PUZZLE 49

The maze below contains four names of actors and actresses. Find four separate routes through the maze without any route crossing another, although they may merge. On each route collect six letters only to give you the names of the four actors and actresses.

FINISH

START

SEE ANSWER 157

142

In a car race the Audi was 3 places ahead
of the Mercedes. The Ferrari was 2 places ahead
of the Renault and the Ligier was somewhere
between the Mercedes and Ferrari.

In what position was the Ligier if
none of the cars were level and
there were only five cars?

SEE ANSWER 163

PUZZLE 51

Complete the square using the letters of P S A L M. When
completed no row, column or diagonal line will contain the same
letter more than once. One horizontal line will spell the word
correctly. What letter should replace the question mark?

			P	
		S		
	A	L		
	M			
				?

SEE ANSWER 130

Take one letter from each segment to find the
name of a city in the USA. What is it?

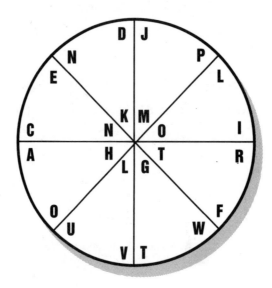

SEE ANSWER 138

PUZZLE 53

The letters surrounding each triangle are the consonants of a
famous sports person's name. The letters inside the triangle have a
connection with each person. What letter should replace the
question mark in the fourth triangle?

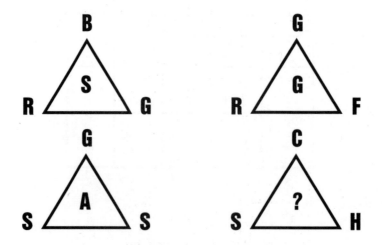

SEE ANSWER 144

PUZZLE 54

Two sides of this pyramid can be seen, but the other two are obscured. Two eight-letter former American presidents are written around the pyramid. Who are they?

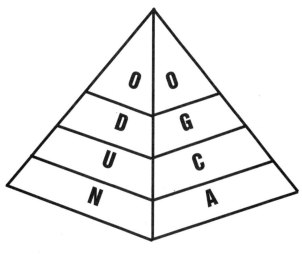

SEE ANSWER 149

PUZZLE 55

A knight, which moves either one square horizontally and two vertically or two horizontally and one vertically, starts at the shaded square of this small chessboard visiting each square without returning to the same square twice. Find the route which spells out six names of people which are also books in the Bible.

L	N	H	A	R	D
U	I	E	A	S	S
I	E	O	A	H	E
J	A	E	A	I	D
S	S	X	U	H	M
E	L	T	U	O	S

SEE ANSWER 154

This is an unusual maze. Find four separate routes through it without any route crossing another, although they may merge. On each route collect 7 letters only to give you four athletes.

FINISH

START

SEE ANSWER 160

PUZZLE 57

At a doctor's office the waiting room was full. The doctor had arranged the appointment times in a special way and the appointments were 10 minutes apart. If Mr. Li has the next appointment in 10 minutes followed by Mr. Nike and then Mr. Lewis, in what order do Mr. Fischer, Mr. Becker and Mr. Schultz go into the surgery?

SEE ANSWER 166

Theo has four cars.
He has a Toyota,
a Mitsubishi
and a Bentley.
Is his fourth car a
Nissan or a Peugeot?

SEE ANSWER 107

PUZZLE 59

If the word PRESIDENTS is

Who are the other presidents?

SEE ANSWER 180

Move from square to touching square – including diagonals – to
discover the name of a famous psychiatrist.

D	E	R	F
U	I	U	D
S	G	M	N

SEE ANSWER 11

PUZZLE 61

In a festival of music pieces, Schuller will be played at 2.00 pm, music by Verdi will be played at 5.06 pm and Schumann will be played at 11.00 pm. At what time will music by Offenbach be played?

SEE ANSWER 19

Rearrange each of the following groups to give the name of a politician or statesman. What are the four names?

IHANGD

ACTORS

HURLCLICH

ANAGRE

SEE ANSWER 60

PUZZLE 63

The names of the following ten fashion designers can be found in this grid on vertical, horizontal and diagonal lines. Can you find them?

Giorgio Armani

Calvin Klein

Hugo Boss

Bruce Oldfield

Jasper Conran

Red or Dead

Ellesse

Stussy

Gucci

Gianni Versace

Y	N	J	Z	B	W	K	X	B	T	N	F	G
G	I	O	R	G	I	O	A	R	M	A	N	I
T	E	S	S	O	B	O	G	U	H	R	G	A
X	L	Y	E	S	V	R	Y	C	R	N	B	N
R	K	Q	S	H	F	X	B	E	V	O	K	N
Z	N	G	S	W	L	J	D	O	Q	C	M	I
J	I	T	E	M	P	O	F	L	W	R	Q	V
Y	V	K	L	K	R	S	B	D	Z	E	S	E
W	L	N	L	D	B	H	P	F	Q	P	D	R
F	A	T	E	G	U	C	C	I	X	S	Y	S
X	C	A	L	T	P	Q	M	E	H	A	W	A
V	D	G	J	V	Z	D	Y	L	G	J	Z	C
S	T	U	S	S	Y	F	K	D	B	J	B	E

SEE ANSWER 29

By taking a segment and finding its pair the names of four
cities of the USA can be made. What are they?

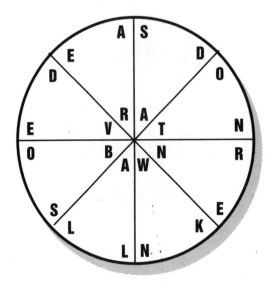

SEE ANSWER 39

PUZZLE 65

In a recipe book there are 8 recipes by Anton Mosimann, 9 by Raymond Blanc and 6 by Albert Roux.

How many Gary Rhodes recipes are there?

SEE ANSWER 45

PUZZLE 66

The vowels have been missed out of the following groups of letters.
Replace the vowels and rearrange each group to form the name of
an American president. Who are the four presidents?

XNN

GRN

NNTLC

MNRT

SEE ANSWER 54

PUZZLE 67

The names of three musical terms have been merged together here.
What are they?

S	G	I	C	H	C
Z					E
R		P	C		E
E			L		A
Z	A	R	I		N
					T
O	O	O	T	D	T

SEE ANSWER 63

151

If the country UNITED STATES is

♈ ♌ ☿ ♓ ♅ ♈   ♑ ♓ ☉ ♓ ♅ ♑

Which are these states?

♋ ☿ ♌ ♌ ♅ ♑ ♍ ♓ ☉
♓ ♅ ♐ ☉ ♑
☉ ♊ ☉ ♑ ♀ ☉
♄ ☉ ♊ ☿ ♀ ♍ ↗ ♌ ☿ ☉
♀ ♊ ♍ ↗ ☿ ♈ ☉
♊ ♍ ♈ ♀ ♑ ♀ ☉ ♌ ☉

SEE ANSWER 68

1B	1A	1D	5C		3D	1A	5C	4E	1D	3D
				▓						
2A	4A	2A	3B		3B	4D	2C	5A	2E	4A

The wordframe above, when filled with the correct letters, will give the name of an athlete. The letters are arranged in the grid below. There are two possible alternatives to fill each square of the wordframe, one correct, the other incorrect. Who is the athlete?

	A	B	C	D	E
1	E	B	U	I	F
2	G	Q	V	J	R
3	H	D	T	S	C
4	A	T	K	U	E
5	L	N	L	P	U

SEE ANSWER 77

What letter is next in this sequence, and why?

C

D

L

N

?

SEE ANSWER 86

PUZZLE 71

Four horses and their jockeys complete a race. Andrew wins the race. Marc is riding Blue Moon. While Redwing finishes last out of the four, Sunshine Boy wins the race. Marc finishes the race in second place. Dan finishes the race after John. Silver Shadow finishes the race after Blue Moon but before Redwing. Who is riding which horse and in what position do they finish?

SEE ANSWER 95

Louis drinks Bollinger champagne, wears Dior clothes, drives a Peugeot and wears a Seiko watch.

Does Louis like to watch Lewis or Tyson fight?

SEE ANSWER 100

Write the following five words related to music in the grid:

CHORD   LENTO   OPERA   PITCH   LARGO

When correctly arranged, another musical word will appear in the middle column. What is it?

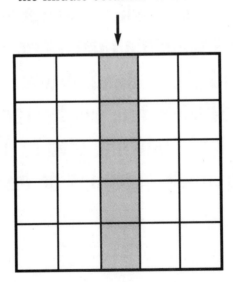

SEE ANSWER 112

Can you work out what letter needs to be inserted in the middle to form four ancient gods, by combining opposite segments?

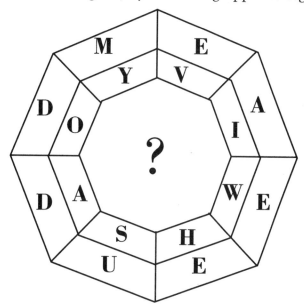

SEE ANSWER 121

PUZZLE 75

Complete the square with the letters of B R Y A N. When completed no row, column or diagonal line will contain the same letter more than once. One horizontal line will spell the name correctly. What letter should replace the question mark?

				N
	N	B		
		A	N	
			Y	
?				

SEE ANSWER 128

155

PUZZLE 76

Take one letter from each segment to find the name of a film star.
Who is it?

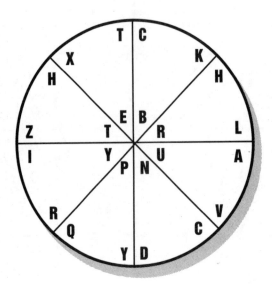

SEE ANSWER 136

PUZZLE 77

What two letters are missing (maybe more than once) from the
connected anagrams below and what is the connection?

REP - -

DGI - - -

RI - -

GRL - -

BURT - -

NTS - - -

SEE ANSWER 83

What letter is missing from the boxes below?

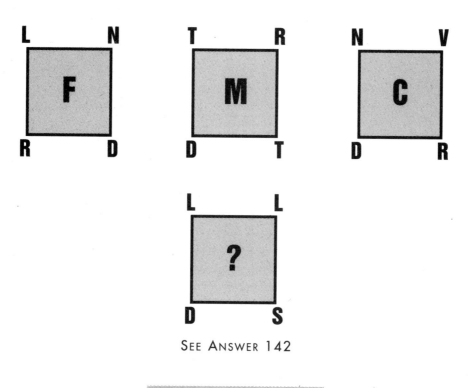

SEE ANSWER 142

PUZZLE 79

Two sides of this pyramid, on a triangular base, can be seen the other one is obscured. Two six letter book names of the Bible are written around the figure. What are they?

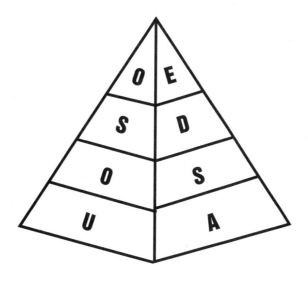

SEE ANSWER 147

PUZZLE 80

A knight, which moves either one square horizontally and two vertically or two horizontally and one vertically, starts at the shaded square of this small chess board visiting each square without returning to the same square twice. Find the route which spells out four famous writers.

A	E	W	N	S	K	L
R	N	M	N	I	E	H
H	I	A	R	P	D	I
E	A	E	S	J	A	A
L	P	E	S	A	N	E
C	T	T	I	O	U	K
E	L	S	S	E	W	G

SEE ANSWER 152

PUZZLE 81

Some letters are missing from this alphabet. Rearrange the missing letters to form the name of a former statesman.

V U X B
Q W G P Z
N K J M H Y

SEE ANSWER 6

A farmer gives names to his cows so that he knows which cows are for beef and which are for dairy products. If Daisy, Lady and Tess are all for dairy products and Mary, Olive and Carol are all for beef, what are Bunny, Ermitrude and Wilma to be used for?

SEE ANSWER 164

PUZZLE 83

This is an unusual maze. Find four separate routes through it without any route crossing another, although the paths may merge. On each route collect 6 letters to give you four musical terms.

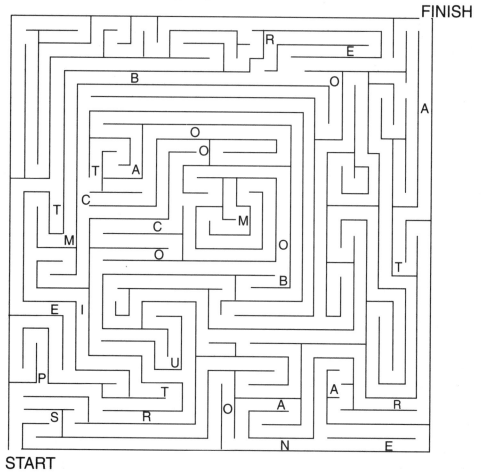

FINISH

START

SEE ANSWER 158

Move from square to touching square – including diagonals – to
discover the name of a singer-actress.

B	A	A	B
R	R	S	R
D	A	T	E
N	A	S	I

SEE ANSWER 14

If a salesman has visited the places below the amount of times
shown, how many times has he visited Alabama?

Alaska = 50
Hawaii = 2
Missouri = 1002
Alabama = ?

SEE ANSWER 22

The names of the following ten furniture makers can be found in this grid on either vertical, horizontal or diagonal lines.
Can you find them?

Adam

Chippendale

Cob

Gillow

Hepplewhite

Lock

Phillipponat

Seddon

Sheraton

Stuart

T	R	Y	J	P	Q	X	G	D	H	K	X
M	A	D	N	V	R	K	F	Z	F	W	Z
J	R	N	O	D	D	E	S	Y	J	O	T
P	S	N	O	T	A	R	E	H	S	Z	F
C	H	E	P	P	L	E	W	H	I	T	E
H	C	H	I	P	P	E	N	D	A	L	E
D	M	B	Y	Z	H	I	S	C	P	G	J
F	T	A	G	W	F	T	L	Y	I	B	M
X	U	K	D	D	U	O	D	L	N	T	X
M	V	C	P	A	C	K	L	W	I	G	K
K	W	G	R	K	M	O	V	R	U	H	Y
Z	H	T	R	X	W	W	B	N	Y	K	P

SEE ANSWER 32

By taking a segment and finding its pair the names of three scientists can be found. Who are they?

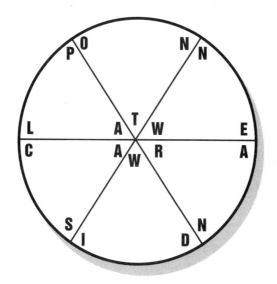

SEE ANSWER 42

There are 41 items of Chippendale furniture, 16 items by Adam and 30 items by Sheraton.

How many items by Gillow are there?

SEE ANSWER 48

The vowels have been missed out of the following groups of letters. Replace the vowels and rearrange each group to form the name of a composer. Who are the four composers?

NDHL

THVBN

LDVV

ZRTM

SEE ANSWER 57

If the names DIEGO MARADONA and JACK CHARLTON are

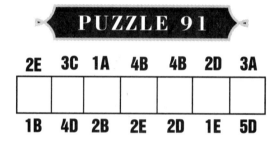

and

Who are the other footballers?

SEE ANSWER 71

2E	3C	1A	4B	4B	2D	3A
1B	4D	2B	2E	2D	1E	5D

The wordframe above, when filled with the correct letters, will give the name of a city in the USA. The letters are arranged in the grid below. There are two possible alternatives to fill each square of the wordframe, one correct, the other incorrect. What is the city?

	A	B	C	D	E
1	I	D	B	F	T
2	Y	N	Q	G	C
3	V	J	H	R	X
4	M	A	E	K	P
5	C	Z	S	O	U

SEE ANSWER 80

PUZZLE 92

What letter should appear next in this series?

2 C 5 F 10 K 14 O 18 S 20 U 25 ?

SEE ANSWER 89

PUZZLE 93

This is an unusual maze. Find four separate routes through it without any route crossing another, although the paths may merge. On each route collect six letters to give you four scientists. Who are they?

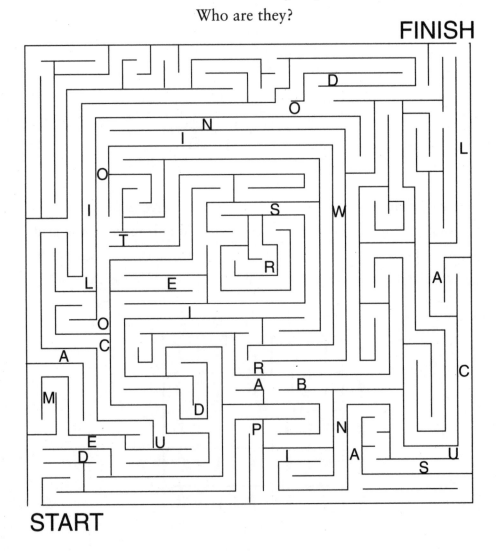

SEE ANSWER 161

Turn the dials on this diagram to give 8 forenames and 8 surnames of famous actresses. Then match them up to give their full names. Who are they? (A score above 5 is very good!)

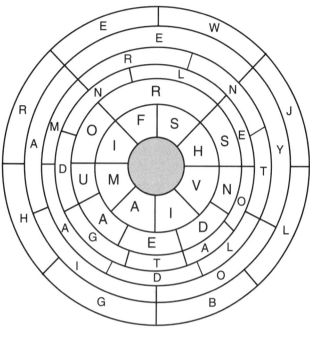

SEE ANSWER 115

Can you work out what letter needs to be inserted in the middle to form four airlines by combining opposite segments?

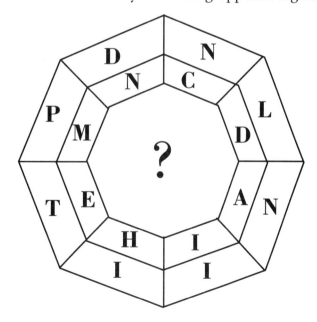

SEE ANSWER 124

Complete the square using the letters of FREUD. When completed
no row, column or diagonal line should contain the same letter
more than once. One row has the letters in the correct order. What
letter will replace the question mark?

		F		
	R		U	
E				
D				
				?

SEE ANSWER 131

Collect one letter from each segment to give the
name of a pop star. Who is it?

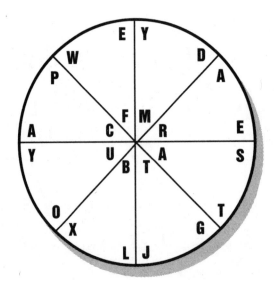

SEE ANSWER 139

A knight, which moves either one square horizontally and two vertically or two horizontally and one vertically, is positioned on this chess board on position A1. If you move to all the squares in the right sequence, without visiting any square twice, you will find the names of five famous golfers.

O	P	C	A	O	R	N
K	A	T	Y	I	P	D
L	M	L	R	C	N	A
R	P	I	Y	M	L	D
W	A	E	K	N	G	O
R	N	E	T	C	L	A
R	A	I	O	F	S	E

SEE ANSWER 155

PUZZLE 99

Rolfe likes Demi Moore and Steffi Graf. He drives a Vauxhall and wears a Casio watch.

Does Rolfe drink Lanson or Laurent Perrier?

SEE ANSWER 103

*A round of drinks were on a table.
Alvin had a Martini, Eric had a
Pernod and Roger had a Brandy.
Can you match the other drinks
to people? Tia Maria, Vodka, Rum,
Whiskey, Ursula, Olga, Harry, Ian.*

SEE ANSWER 167

PUZZLE 101

The names of the following ten film stars can be found in this grid
on vertical, horizontal and diagonal lines. Can you find them?

John Cleese

Tom Cruise

Mel Gibson

Hugh Grant

Tom Hanks

Val Kilmer

Bruce Lee

Al Pacino

Sean Penn

Brad Pitt

W	Z	Q	E	P	R	V	H	E	F	M
T	O	U	S	Y	J	A	H	E	E	Z
T	N	S	I	G	K	L	U	L	S	W
I	I	E	U	F	H	K	G	E	E	P
P	C	A	R	H	X	I	H	C	E	H
D	A	N	C	H	B	L	G	U	L	J
A	P	P	M	S	Q	M	R	R	C	R
R	L	E	O	J	R	E	A	B	N	G
B	A	N	T	T	Z	R	N	P	H	Y
S	K	N	A	H	M	O	T	W	O	S
Y	R	B	X	F	Q	J	X	N	J	S

SEE ANSWER 35

In a gallery, painting number 2105 is by Edvard Munch, painting number 1650 is by Claude Monet and painting number 151 is by Pablo Picasso.

What number is the painting by Salvador Dali?

SEE ANSWER 25

How far should it be to Las Vegas on this strange signpost?

SEE ANSWER 51

If the name ELIZABETH TAYLOR is

Who are the other legendary film stars?

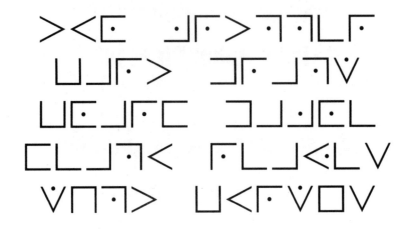

SEE ANSWER 74

PUZZLE 105

Two series are merged together here. Which two letters
should appear next in this series?

D V H Q L L P G T ? ?

Lena drives a Volkswagen. She wears White Linen perfume and her preferred chef is Gary Rhodes. Who would be her first choice dress designer, Jasper Conran or Jurgen Lehl?

SEE ANSWER 106

PUZZLE 107

Turn the dials on this diagram to reveal 13 musical terms.
A score above 8 is very good.

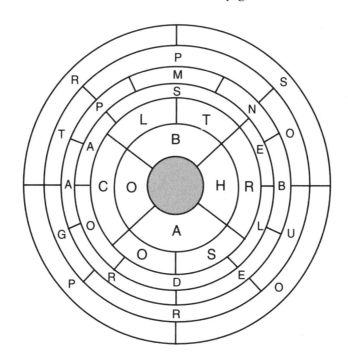

SEE ANSWER 118

George Michael has sold 1151 CDs, Bruce Springsteen has sold 101 and Simple Minds have sold 2552. How many have Simply Red sold?

SEE ANSWER 26

PUZZLE 109

The names of the following ten car manufacturers can be found in this grid on vertical, horizontal and diagonal lines. Can you find them?

Citroen

Jaguar

Peugeot

Renault

Rolls Royce

Rover

Skoda

Toyota

Volkswagen

Yugo

R	N	B	L	F	K	X	C	D	R
E	N	D	C	W	Q	H	S	O	E
N	E	G	A	W	S	K	L	O	V
A	O	H	J	K	O	L	B	P	O
U	R	G	V	D	S	F	Y	J	R
L	T	C	A	R	A	U	G	A	J
T	I	T	O	E	G	U	E	P	M
P	C	Y	T	O	Y	O	T	A	B
J	C	F	V	G	Z	C	W	D	K
E	K	D	P	M	H	Q	G	Y	F

SEE ANSWER 36

Some letters are missing from this alphabet. Rearrange the missing letters to form the name of a river.

C F I W O U X
J V Q R K
L P B M S H
D

SEE ANSWER 4

Complete the square using the letters of T E X A S. When completed no row, column or diagonal line should contain the same letter more than once. One horizontal line will spell the name correctly. What letter will replace the question mark?

		T		
		E	X	
		A		
	S			
		X		?

SEE ANSWER 129

PUZZLE 112

Collect one letter from each segment to give the
name of a book in the Bible. What is it?

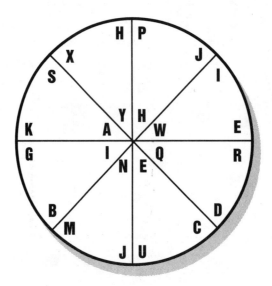

SEE ANSWER 137

PUZZLE 113

What letter has been missed from the last box?

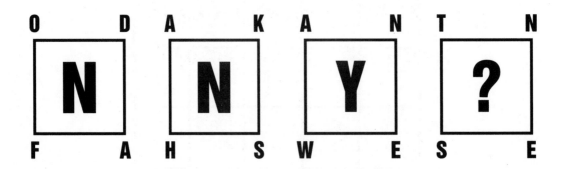

SEE ANSWER 143

Move from square to touching square – including diagonals – to discover the name of an American state.

E	P	N	S
I	N	Y	L
A	N	A	V

SEE ANSWER 12

PUZZLE 115

A bar sold

500 measures of brandy,
1000 measures of rum
and just 1 measure of Gin.

How many measures of
whiskey did it sell?

SEE ANSWER 20

The names of the following ten watch manufacturers can be found in this grid on vertical, horizontal and diagonal lines. Can you find them?

Casio

Gucci

Ingersoll

Limit

Rotary

Rolex

Seiko

Sekonda

Timex

Tissot

H	P	C	T	U	B	O	P	M	I
G	U	C	C	I	Q	K	F	N	J
M	B	K	W	T	M	I	G	T	C
J	N	P	A	C	O	E	Z	D	V
Q	X	V	D	A	R	S	X	Q	Y
Z	R	X	N	S	F	X	S	K	R
D	K	E	O	I	M	B	F	I	A
V	X	L	K	O	L	I	M	I	T
P	L	O	E	Y	Q	W	J	V	O
J	F	R	S	B	M	K	U	P	R

SEE ANSWER 30

By taking a segment and finding its pair, four film stars can be found. Who are they?

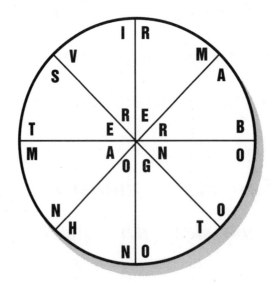

SEE ANSWER 40

Along a street there are 7 Ford cars, 9 Toyota cars and 13 Alfa Romeo cars.

How many Mazda cars are there?

SEE ANSWER 46

PUZZLE 119

The vowels have been missed out of the following groups of letters.
Replace the vowels and rearrange each group to form the name
of a film star. Who are the four stars?

STND FFMHN

VST RNMT

TRCPK YZSW

LMN FFGTHRS

SEE ANSWER 55

PUZZLE 120

The names of three lakes have been merged together here.
Which are they?

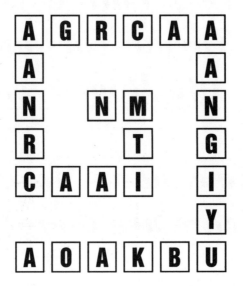

SEE ANSWER 64

PUZZLE 121

If the term ANCIENT GODS is

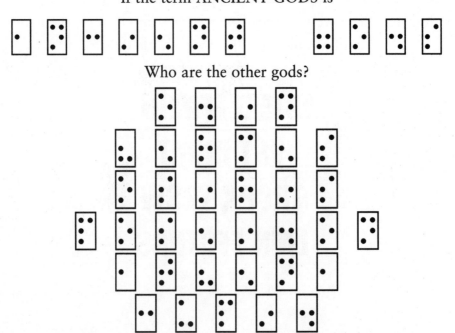

Who are the other gods?

SEE ANSWER 69

1E	2C	3D		3A	4E	2D	5D	3B	1C
4A	5B	1B		1C	5B	4E	2C	4C	3D

The wordframe above, when filled with the correct letters, will give the name of a film star. The letters are arranged in the grid below. There are two possible alternatives to fill each square of the wordframe, one correct, the other incorrect. Who is the film star?

	A	B	C	D	E
1	A	L	R	F	M
2	Q	J	E	H	C
3	G	Y	P	N	W
4	D	Z	O	K	B
5	T	I	V	S	X

SEE ANSWER 78

What letters are missing from this sequence?

A S ? ? G H J

SEE ANSWER 87

Six people go into a store through the underground car park going to floors 1, 2, 3, 4, 5 and 6. Each person goes to a different floor in the same elevator, which goes up stopping at each floor. Eddie's ride is the longest. Angie gets out before Frankie but after Debbie. Charlie gets out first. Barbie leaves before Debbie, who leaves at the third floor.

At what floor does each person leave?

SEE ANSWER 96

Jean is a relation of the scientist Jenner. Jean was born in Denver but now lives in Seattle.

Is Jean is a bigger fan of tennis player Sampras or McEnroe?

SEE ANSWER 101

The people listed below were told that they could win a car if they could arrange their names in the grid below to give the car's manufacturer down the shaded column. What car did they get? Their names were:

BRUCE DIANA SARAH BRIAN BILLY MARIE

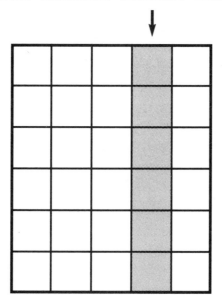

SEE ANSWER 113

Two sides of this pyramid can be seen, but the other two are obscured. Two eight-letter American states are written around the pyramid. What are they?

SEE ANSWER 148

PUZZLE 128

A knight, which moves either one square horizontally and two vertically or two horizontally and one vertically, starts at the shaded square of this chess board visiting each square without returning to the same square twice. Find the route which spells out six famous movie stars.

O	T	E	S	I	O	T	I
M	O	P	S	L	B	G	R
E	O	G	N	D	N	G	O
N	E	B	O	R	A	I	O
H	V	E	J	D	L	M	T
S	R	A	E	F	D	R	N
E	W	B	U	A	I	R	C
O	I	M	N	E	R	E	T

SEE ANSWER 153

PUZZLE 129

This list of English monarchs shows the fictitious number of years they reigned. Can you think of a monarch who would have reigned for less than a year?

Mary	**17**
James	**12**
George	**10**
Charles	**7**
William	**3**

SEE ANSWER 170

In a large raffle Ian had ticket number one, Vivian had number twelve and David had number 1006.

Who of the following had ticket numbers 500, 60, 1000 and 151 from Axel, Charlie, Brenda and Norman?

SEE ANSWER 165

PUZZLE 131

Some letters are missing from this alphabet. Rearrange the missing letters to form the name of a European city.

M W D
Y Q
Z P
I
O K J
L V
X F G
N

SEE ANSWER 7

Move from square to touching square – including diagonals – to discover the name of a car.

O	R	L	K
B	A	G	N
M	H	I	I

SEE ANSWER 15

PUZZLE 133

If Beckenbauer made 100 appearances for his country and Littbarski made 52 and Völler made 105, how many appearances did Hässler make?

SEE ANSWER 23

The names of the following ten perfumes can be found in this grid on vertical, horizontal and diagonal lines. Can you find them?

Amarige

Anais Anais

Coco

Dune

Miss Dior

Obsession

Paris

Safari

Samsara

Spellbound

S	I	A	N	A	S	I	A	N	A
A	P	D	G	H	F	P	J	C	R
F	C	E	G	I	R	A	M	A	A
A	F	H	L	D	J	R	K	F	S
R	Y	Q	U	L	Z	I	Z	R	M
I	R	N	Z	X	B	S	F	X	A
Q	E	V	K	W	O	O	Y	J	S
B	H	K	V	D	W	C	U	G	I
O	B	S	E	S	S	I	O	N	G
R	O	I	D	S	S	I	M	C	D

SEE ANSWER 33

*If there have been
13 Malaysia Airline flights,
22 Virgin Atlantic flights and
16 Pan Am flights this week,
how many Cathay Pacific
flights have there been?*

SEE ANSWER 49

PUZZLE 136

The names of five pop groups are written here in code. What are they?

i) **10 6 22 22 13**

ii) **8 18 14 11 15 2 9 22 23**

iii) **25 12 13 17 12 5 18**

iv) **20 22 13 22 8 18 8**

v) **8 18 14 11 15 22 14 18 13 23 8**

See Answer 72

PUZZLE 137

What letter should appear next in this series?

A E F H I K ?

See Answer 90

PUZZLE 138

Olga lives in Canada and attended the University of Winnipeg. She most enjoys listening to singer George Michael.

Is her perfume Coco or Dune?

SEE ANSWER 104

PUZZLE 139

Turn the dial on this diagram to give 11 names of lakes from around the world. (7 or over is a good score.)

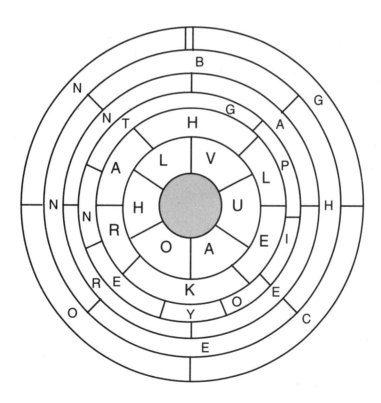

SEE ANSWER 116

Can you work out what letter needs to be inserted in the middle to form four artists by combining opposite segments?

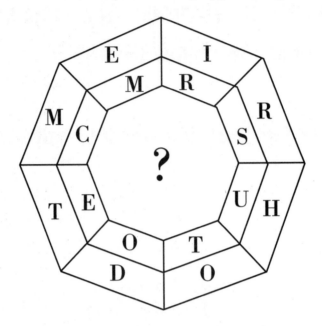

SEE ANSWER 125

Complete the square using the letters of L O T U S. When completed no row, column or diagonal line should contain the same letter more than once. One horizontal line will spell the flower correctly. What letter will replace the question mark?

?				
				O
			T	U
			S	L
				T

SEE ANSWER 132

Some letters are missing from this alphabet. Rearrange the missing letters to form the name of a Mexican city.

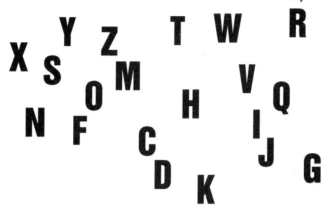

SEE ANSWER 5

If the owner of the Mercedes is Dave, the owner of the Nissan is Simon and the owner of the Porsche is Colin, can you find the owners of the remaining cars from the people listed?

Cars: Toyota, Rover, Jaguar, Fiat and Honda.

People: Nigel, Irene, Vera, Oliver and Ursula.

SEE ANSWER 168

If Mercury is linked with Fillmore, Jupiter with Carter, Saturn with Ford and Uranus with Arthur, which of the following presidents would be linked with Charon?

i)   Lincoln

ii) Adams

iii) Monroe

iv) Buchanan

v)   Hoover

SEE ANSWER 173

PUZZLE 145

If London has 550 visitors, Budapest has 500 and Madrid has 2001, how many visitors does Paris have?

SEE ANSWER 21

PUZZLE 146

The names of the following ten tennis players can be found in this grid on vertical, horizontal and diagonal lines. Can you find them?

Jeremy Bates

Pat Cash

Wayne Ferreira

Ivan Lendl

Jana Novotna

Marc Rosset

Greg Rusedski

Monica Seles

Michael Stich

Helena Sukova

C	J	H	J	K	I	M	F	G	I	M	C	W
B	E	C	M	Z	K	Y	X	B	V	N	A	Y
J	R	I	A	O	S	J	V	H	A	Y	V	S
F	E	T	R	N	D	C	Y	V	N	D	O	E
K	M	S	C	H	E	P	H	E	L	K	K	L
G	Y	L	R	D	S	K	F	P	E	J	U	E
Z	B	E	O	X	U	E	G	A	N	M	S	S
C	A	A	S	W	R	W	B	T	D	D	A	A
P	T	H	S	R	G	M	W	C	L	Z	N	C
J	E	C	E	F	E	Y	V	A	Y	B	E	I
F	S	I	T	Y	R	Z	M	S	J	X	L	N
H	R	M	P	H	G	C	B	H	K	F	E	O
A	N	T	O	V	O	N	A	N	A	J	H	M

SEE ANSWER 31

PUZZLE 147

By taking a segment and finding its pair the names of four musical terms can be found. What are they?

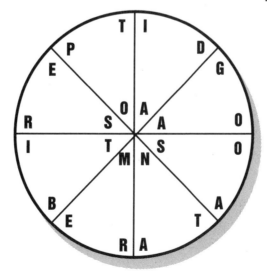

SEE ANSWER 41

The vowels have been missed out of the following groups of letters.
Replace the vowels and rearrange each group to form the name
of a female singer. Who are the four singers?

NN LNXN

NJT CSKJN

RHM RYC

KLY GMN

SEE ANSWER 56

The price of champagne in a store in England is shown here.
How much will Dom Perignon cost?

Bollinger	£9.40
Laurent Perrier	£18.00
Perrier Jouet	£16.00
Dom Perignon	£ ?

SEE ANSWER 47

PUZZLE 150

The names of two actors have been merged together here.
Who are they?

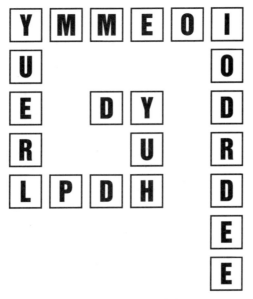

SEE ANSWER 65

PUZZLE 151

If the word SCIENTIST is

who are these scientists?

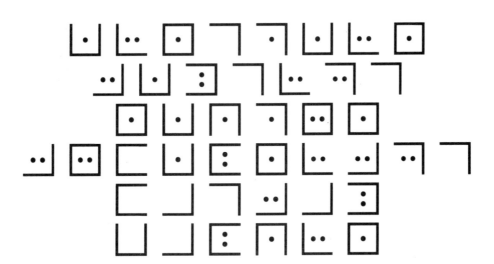

SEE ANSWER 70

1D	2A	5E		2C	3B	2E	4B	5A	1A	1B	4A
			▓								
2C	4B	3B		1E	4C	1A	3D	2C	3E	4D	5C

The wordframe above, when filled with the correct letters, will give the name of a female athlete. The letters are arranged in the grid below. There are two possible alternatives to fill each square of the wordframe, one correct, the other incorrect.

Who is the athlete?

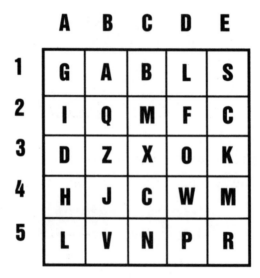

	A	B	C	D	E
1	G	A	B	L	S
2	I	Q	M	F	C
3	D	Z	X	O	K
4	H	J	C	W	M
5	L	V	N	P	R

SEE ANSWER 79

Some letters are missing from this alphabet. Rearrange the missing letters to form the name of a scientist.

SEE ANSWER 1

PUZZLE 154

What letter should appear next in this series?

M V E M J S U N

SEE ANSWER 88

PUZZLE 155

Complete the square using the letters of L E W I S. When completed no row, column or diagonal line should contain the same letter more than once. One horizontal line should spell the name correctly. What letter will replace the question mark?

	W			
	L	E		
	I	S		
				?

SEE ANSWER 133

Paul wears Levi jeans, he travels on United Airlines and he thinks Anthony Hopkins is a great actor.

Does Paul drive a Porsche or a Jaguar?

SEE ANSWER 102

PUZZLE 157

Turn the dials on this unusual safe to give
12 surnames of sports stars from the past and present.
(More than 8 is a good score.)

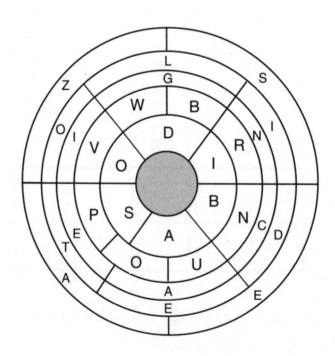

SEE ANSWER 114

Can you work out what letter needs to be inserted in the middle to form four sporting champions by combining opposite segments?

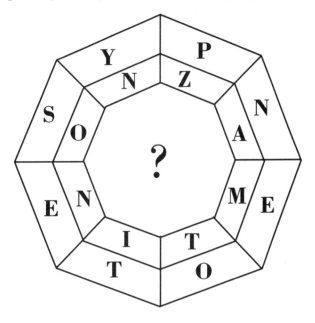

SEE ANSWER 123

Move from square to touching square – including diagonals – to discover the name of an order of monks.

E	N	I	C
E	D	E	T
J	N	I	B

SEE ANSWER 16

In a drawer at an international bank there are:

100 Francs

600 Dollars

500 Rands

How many Lira are there?

SEE ANSWER 24

PUZZLE 161

The names of the following ten airlines can be found in this grid on vertical, horizontal and diagonal lines. Can you find them?

Aer Lingus
Aeroflot
Alitalia
Delta
Egypt Air
Finnair
Lufthansa
Monarch
Olympic
Swissair

O	B	X	R	C	Y	Y	K	H	A
L	L	G	I	R	X	T	B	E	P
Y	U	Z	A	I	G	O	R	P	F
M	F	C	T	A	T	L	E	D	H
P	T	Y	P	N	I	F	D	Z	C
I	H	Q	Y	N	V	O	M	W	R
C	A	K	G	I	R	F	K	A
B	N	U	E	F	D	E	K	V	N
H	S	W	I	S	S	A	I	R	O
Z	A	L	I	T	A	L	I	A	M

SEE ANSWER 34

PUZZLE 162

Perfume manufacturers are bringing out new fragrances for the coming season.

Ralph Lauren has four new fragrances, Christian Dior has five and Givenchy has two new fragrances.

How many new scents will be promoted by Yves Saint Laurent?

See Answer 50

PUZZLE 163

The names of five authors are written here in code.
Who are they?

i) TUFQIFO LJOH
ii) BHBUIB DISJTUJF
iii) KPIO HSJTIBN
iv) DIBSMFT EJDLFOT
v) HFPSHF PSXFMM

See Answer 73

Some letters are missing from this alphabet. Rearrange the missing letters to form the name of a composer.

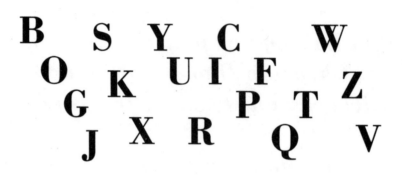

SEE ANSWER 8

What letter should appear next in this series?

Z

X

U

Q

L

SEE ANSWER 91

Emma drinks Benedictine, she reads books by Sigmund Freud and holidays in Miami.

Is her hero Muhammad Ali or George Best?

SEE ANSWER 105

Turn the dials on this diagram to give 8 forenames and 8 family names of famous actors. Then match them up to give their full names. Who are they? (A score above 5 is very good.)

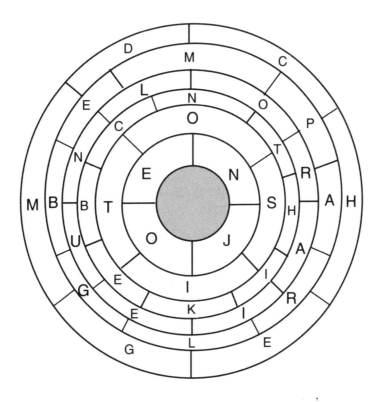

SEE ANSWER 117

There are eight floors in a high-rise block. The fifth floor has the only apartment with two bedrooms. Mrs Barber has a baby and cannot carry a buggy upstairs when the elevator is out of order. Mr and Mrs Elder also find climbing difficult now they are retired. Mr Archer likes the peace and quiet of living on the top floor. Mrs Cook and her daughter need a two-bedroom flat. Mr and Mrs Hooper live just below Mr Archer. Mrs Cook lives above Mr Gardener and below Mrs Driver. Mr and Mrs Fisher live above Mr and Mrs Elder.

Who lives where?

SEE ANSWER 97

The following fictitious compound is primarily made up of the following elements. Two large components, however, have been omitted: what percentage does the compound have of gold and silver?

Al	=	22%
Sn	=	10%
Pt	=	8%
Fe	=	2%
Ag	=	??
Au	=	??

SEE ANSWER 178

If Henry drives a Mercedes, Tom drives a Honda, Sally drives a
Mazda and Richard drives a Lincoln, what will car Brenda drive?

i)   Cadillac
ii)   Ford
iii)   Audi
iv)   Citroen
v)   Alfa
vi)   Triumph
vii)   Saab

SEE ANSWER 175

Complete the square using the letters of T U R I N. When
completed no row, column or diagonal line should contain the same
letter more than once. One horizontal line should spell the city
correctly. What letter will replace the question mark?

	N		U	
?				
			R	
				U

SEE ANSWER 172

The serial numbers for these products all relate to their names?
What is the name of the last product?

NAME	SERIAL NO
HABBIZ	82249.62
EDDAN	5842.41
BACCAR	22361.81
?	94989.42

SEE ANSWER 177

PUZZLE 173

These four robots will only operate when the
correct code is programmed into their mainframes.
Which one will not work and why?

Exell   **0110**
Lidex   **0111**
Maxis   **1011**
Vamov   **1010**

SEE ANSWER 174

Rearrange these boxes in a 3 x 3 square in such a way that the adjoining letters are always the same. Then add the alphanumeric values of each line of three outer letters and convert back to letters to give the name of a Roman god.

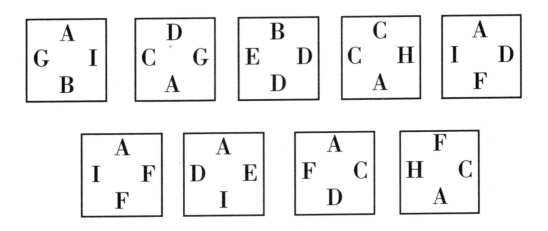

SEE ANSWER 171

PUZZLE 175

The letters around each box and the one in the middle all have an American link. Which letters replace the question marks?

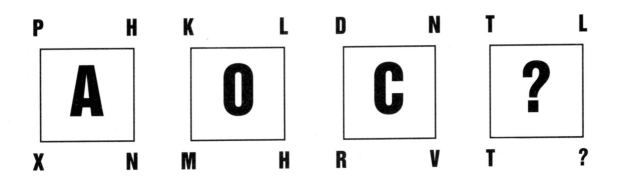

SEE ANSWER 179

PUZZLE 176

Some letters are missing from this alphabet. Rearrange the missing letters to form the name of a state in the USA.

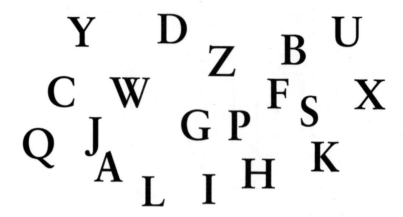

SEE ANSWER 3

PUZZLE 177

Here is a strange signpost to the burial grounds in Ancient Egypt. How far is it to burial ground of Thoth?

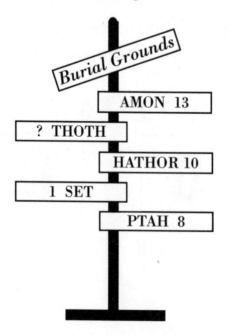

SEE ANSWER 169

Move from square to touching square – including diagonals – to
discover the name of an actor.

S	T	W	O	O
A	T	C	I	O
E	L	N	L	D

SEE ANSWER 13

When manned space travel began, a piece of space material
collected by cosmonauts contained a strange riddle.

Property of NEPTUNE

This is our NINTH expedition

A party of SEVEN astronauts

Setting up our IMPERIAL base

Over a period of FIFTY-ONE days

There followed a picture a dead US President.
Who was it?

(i) Adams (ii) Harrison (iii) Jackson (iv) Monroe (v) Van Buren

SEE ANSWER 176

This is an unusual maze. Find four separate routes through it
without any route crossing another, although the paths may merge.
On each route collect 6 letters to give you four cities in the USA.

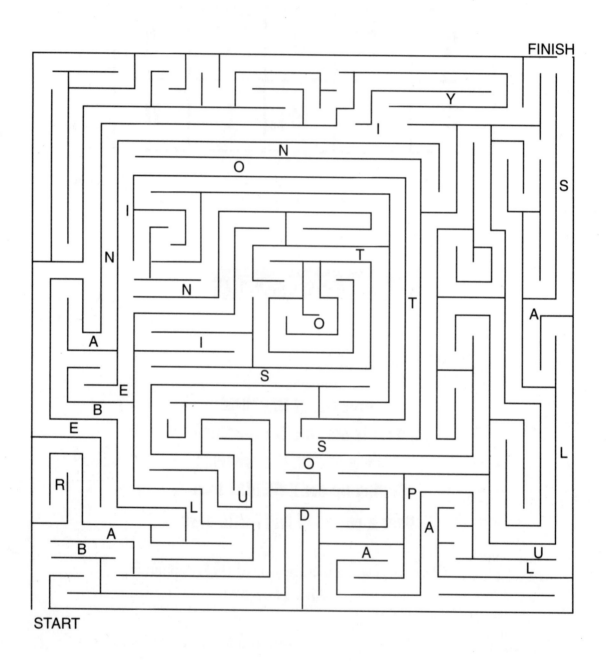

FINISH

START

SEE ANSWER 159

1   Hawking.

2   Renault.

3   Vermont.

4   Yangtze.

5   Puebla.

6   Fidel Castro.

7   Bucharest.

8   Handel.

9   Copenhagen.

10   Tchaikovsky.

11   Sigmund Freud.

12   Pennsylvania.

13   Clint Eastwood.

14   Barbra Streisand.

15   Lamborghini.

16   Benedictine.

17   1003. The Roman numerals in each name are added together.

18   1. The Roman numerals in each are added together.

19   1.00 pm. The Roman numerals in each name are added together. A point is then placed two places in to give a time.

20   1. The Roman numerals in each drink give the amount.

21   1. The Roman numerals in each name are added together.

22   1050. The Roman numerals are added together in each place name.

23   50. The Roman numerals are added together in each name.

24   51. The Roman numerals are added together to give the amounts.

25   1106. The Roman numerals in each name are added together.

26   1551. The Roman numerals in each name are added together.

27

T	N	A	R	G	D	N	U	M	A	S	O	R
B	Y	N	L	K	L	Q	O	X	C	B	O	A
Q	W	T	F	Z	P	H	K	U	J	B	G	Y
Y	G	H	V	S	N	X	E	O	R	C	M	
D	V	O	W	E	M	D	I	R	S	U	K	O
J	K	N	K	D	B	P	T	T	U	N	O	N
P	M	Y	S	O	S	C	H	R	C	O	P	D
P	F	T	Y	H	A	Y	F	E	O	L	J	B
Z	W	O	U	R	Z	G	L	B	B	O	C	L
F	C	B	R	Y	Q	K	O	L	L	U	F	A
Y	V	I	D	R	J	F	Y	A	U	B	R	N
W	E	N	V	A	Y	Q	D	P	A	E	W	C
R	G	K	P	G	R	Z	B	Y	P	T	P	Q

28

B	G	J	B	F	H	C	L	G	B
D	E	U	T	Z	E	A	A	O	M
C	T	V	H	W	N	P	L	S	F
P	R	V	E	S	R	L	A	S	H
S	A	L	O	N	I	Q	Y	E	K
K	N	N	J	N	O	X	A	T	D
B	I	W	G	V	T	G	Q	B	W
D	U	E	Z	K	F	X	E	Y	G
F	R	E	G	O	R	L	O	P	Y
Q	G	X	V	C	H	X	Z	O	D

29

```
Y N J Z B W K X B T N F G
G I O R G I O A R M A N I
T E S S O B O G U H R G A
X L V E S V R Y C R N B N
R K Q S H F X B E V O K N
Z N G S W L J D O Q C M I
J I T E M P O F L W R Q V
Y V K L K R S B D Z E S E
W L N L D B H P F Q P D R
F A T E G U C C I X S Y S
X C A L T P Q M E H A W A
V D G J V Z D Y L G J Z C
S T U S S Y F K D B J B E
```

30

```
H P C T U B O P M I
G U C C I Q K F N J
M B K W T M I G T C
J N P A C O E Z D V
Q X V D A R S X Q Y
Z R X N S F X S K R
D K E O I M B F I A
V X L K O L I M I T
P L O E Y Q W J V O
J F R S B M K U P R
```

31

```
C J H J K I M F G I M C W
B E C M Z K Y X B V N A Y
J R I A O S J V H A Y V S
F E T R N D C Y V N D O E
K M S C H E P H E L K K L
G Y L R D S K F P E J U E
Z B E O X U E G A N M S S
C A A S W R W B T D D A A
P T H S R G M W C L Z N C
J E C E F E Y V A Y B E I
F S I T Y R Z M S J X L N
H R M P H G C B H K F E Q
A N T O V O N A N A J H M
```

32

```
T R Y J P Q X G D H K X
M A D N V R K F Z F W Z
J R N O D D E S Y J O T
P S N O T A R E H S Z F
C H E P P L E W H I T E
H C H I P P E N D A L E
D M B Y Z H I S C P G J
F T A G W F T L Y I B M
X U K R D U O D L N T X
M V C P A C K L W I G K
K W G R K M O V R U H Y
Z H T R X W W B N Y K P
```

33

```
S I A N A S I A N A
A P D G H F P J C R
F C E G I R A M A A
A F H L D J R K F S
R Y Q U L Z I Z R M
I R N Z X B S F X A
Q E V K W O O Y J S
B H K V D W C U G I
O B S E S S I O N G
R O I D S S I M C D
```

34

```
O B X R C Y Y K H A
L L G I R X T B E P
Y U Z A I G O R P F
M F C T A T L E D H
P T Y P N I F D Z C
I H Q Y N V O M W R
C A K G I X R F K A
B N U E F D E K V N
H S W I S S A I R O
Z A L I T A L I A M
```

35

```
W Z Q E P R V H E F M
T O U S Y J A H E E Z
T N S I G K L U L S W
I I E U F H K G E E P
P C A R H X I H C E H
D A N C H B L G U L J
A P P M S Q M R R C R
R L E O J R E A B N G
B A N T T Z R N P H Y
S K N A H M O T W O S
Y R B X F Q J X N J S
```

36

```
R N B L F K X C D R
E N D C W Q H S O E
N E G A W S K L O V
A O H J K O L B P O
U R G V D S F Y J R
L T C A R A U G A J
T I T O E G U E P M
P C Y T O Y O T A B
J C F V G Z C W D K
E K D P M H Q G Y F
```

37 Daniel, Exodus, Isaiah and Joshua can be found by pairing alternate segments.

38 Agassi, Becker, Hingis and Muster can be found by pairing adjacent segments.

39 Boston, Dallas, Denver and Newark can be found by pairing opposite segments.

40 Bogart, Heston, Marvin and Monroe can be found by pairing alternate segments.

41 Adagio, Presto, Sonata and Timbre can be found by pairing adjacent segments.

42 Darwin, Newton and Pascal can be found by pairing adjacent segments.

43 50. The number of letters in each name, multiplied by 10, gives the amount.

44 9. The alphabetical position of the last letter of the name gives the amount.

45 7. The consonants in each name gives the number of recipes.

46 8. Each vowel is given a value of one and each consonant is give a value of two. These are added together in each name to give the amount.

47 13. The alphanumeric values of the letters in each champagne are added together. The total is divided by 10 to give the price.

48 22. In each name a vowel is given a value of five and a consonant is given a value of three. These are added together to give the amount.

49 3. The alphabetical position of the first letter gives the amount.

50 Six. The number of vowels in each name give the amount.

51 340. Each vowel is given a value of 30 and each consonant is given a value of 50. These are added together in each city name to give the distance.

52 Budapest
London
Stockholm
Madrid

53 Pennsylvania
Massachusetts
Connecticut
Minnesota

54 Nixon
Reagan
Clinton
Truman

55 Dustin Hoffman
Steve Martin
Patrick Swayze
Melanie Griffiths

56 Annie Lennox
Janet Jackson
Mariah Carey
Kylie Minogue

57 Handel
Beethoven
Vivaldi
Mozart

58 Brooklyn because it is a city, the others are states (Florida, Delaware and Arizona).

59 Spielberg. The others are scientists: Archimedes, Galileo and Einstein.

60 Gandhi
Castro
Churchill
Reagan

61 Gunnell
Backley
Johnson

62 Travolta
Stallone
Goldberg

63 Pizzicato
Crescendo
Larghetto

64 Nicaragua
Maracaibo
Tanganyka

65 Dudley Moore and Eddie Murphy.

66 (The alphabet is 6 letters out of phase)
   i)   Pat Cash
  ii)   Steffi Graf
 iii)   Andre Agassi
 iv)   Martina Navratilova
  v)   Conchita Martinez

67
   i)   Bill Clinton
  ii)   Abraham Lincoln
 iii)   George Washington
 iv)   Harry S. Truman
  v)   John F. Kennedy
 vi)   Ulysses Grant

68
   i)   Minnesota
  ii)   Texas
 iii)   Alaska
 iv)   California
  v)   Florida
 vi)   Louisiana

69
   i)   Odin
  ii)   Hermes
 iii)   Osiris
 iv)   Poseidon
  v)   Athena
 vi)   Cupid

70
   i)   Einstein
  ii)   Celsius
 iii)   Newton
 iv)   Copernicus
  v)   Pascal
 vi)   Darwin

71
   i)   Roberto Baggio
  ii)   Dennis Bergkamp
 iii)   Kevin Keegan
 iv)   Eric Cantona
  v)   Jurgen Klinsmann

72
   i)   Queen
  ii)   Simply Red
 iii)   Bon Jovi
 iv)   Genesis
  v)   Simple Minds

73
 i)   Stephen King
 ii) Agatha Christie
 iii) John Grisham
 iv) Charles Dickens
 v)   George Orwell

74
 i)   Yul Brynner
 ii) Cary Grant
 iii) Clark Gable
 iv) Keanu Reaves
 v)   Tony Curtis

75   Bob Marley.

76   Michael Chang.

77   Gail Devers.

78   Mel Gibson.

79   Liz McColgan.

80   Chicago.

81   O and N. They all are scientists: Newton, Young, Edison, Rontgen

82   O and N. The stars are: Collins, Lennon, Jones, Diamond and Jackson.

83   A and O. These are all musical terms: Opera, Adagio, Aria, Largo, Rubato and Sonata.

84   Q. The alphabet is moved five letters, then four, then three, etc.

85   T and V. The alphabet with the following sequence of spaces between the letters: two, three, two, four, two, five and two.

86   W. The letters are in alphabetical sequence, no straight lines, one straight line etc.)

87   D and F. On a Qwerty keyboard, these are the first letters, reading from the left, of the middle row.

88   P. They are the initials of the planets: Mercury, Venus, Earth, Mars, Jupiter, Saturn, Uranus, Neptune and Pluto.

89   Z. Each letter is one alphabetical place after the number.

90   L. The letters are those which only contain straight lines

91   F. The letters are the alphabet in reverse, firstly missing one letter, then two, then three etc.

92   X and B. Every fourth letter of the alphabet forms one series and every fifth letter from the end of the alphabet forms the other series. These are merged together.

93   Finishing order is 12, 3, 11, 21, 7 and 8 last.

94

Mr Evans	Mrs Graves	Mrs Davis	Mr Adams
Mrs Harris	Mrs Bates	Mr Francis	Mr Conners

95   Andrew on Sunshine Boy wins the race, Marc on Blue Moon comes second, John on Silver Shadow is third and Dan on Redwing finishes last.

96 Charlie leaves at the 1st floor.
Barbie leaves at the 2nd floor.
Debbie leaves at the 3rd floor.
Angie leaves at the 4th floor.
Frankie leaves at the 5th floor.
Eddie leaves at the 6th floor.

97 8th floor – Mr Archer
7th floor – Mr and Mrs Hooper
6th floor – Mrs Driver
5th floor – Mrs Cook and daughter
4th floor – Mr Gardener
3rd floor – Mr and Mrs Fisher
2nd floor – Mr and Mrs Elder
1st floor – Mrs Baker

98 Monarch. The first letters placed together give the name of Adam.

99 Martina Navratilova. The last letters placed together give the name Laura.

100 Tyson. The third letters placed together give the name Louis.

101 McEnroe. The first letter of the first word gives the first letter of Jean. The second letter of the second word gives the second letter of Jean and so on.

102 Porsche. The first letters, when placed together in reverse order, give the name Paul.

103 Laurent Perrier. The last letters, when placed together in reverse order, give the name Rolfe.

104 Coco. The last letters, when placed in reverse order, read Olga.

105 Muhammad Ali. The fourth letters when placed together read Emma.

106 A. Jurgen Lehl. The last letter of the last word gives the first of Lena, the penultimate letter of the penultimate word gives the second of Lena, and so on.

107 Peugeot. The penultimate letters in each car name give Theo.

108 Each of the four names contains the name of Chinese Dynasty. They are: Wei, Chin, Han and Tang.

109 (i) Add Joel to get John Lennon.
(ii) Add Job to get Bon Jovi.
(iii) Add Amos to get Alison Moyet.

110 Lira

I	L	L	I	N	O	I	S
M	I	C	H	I	G	A	N
A	R	K	A	N	S	A	S
M	A	R	Y	L	A	N	D

111 Tony Curtis.

C	O	P	P	E	R
M	U	R	P	H	Y
M	A	R	V	I	N
M	A	R	T	I	N
G	A	R	C	I	A
R	E	E	V	E	S

112   Tenor.

P	I	T	C	H
O	P	E	R	A
L	E	N	T	O
C	H	O	R	D
L	A	R	G	O

113   Lancia.

B	I	L	L	Y
B	R	I	A	N
D	I	A	N	A
B	R	U	C	E
M	A	R	I	E
S	A	R	A	H

114   Spitz, Borg, Bowe, Lewis, Ali, Pele, Zico, Senna, Lauda, Bats, David, Coe.

115   Holly Hunter, Sally Field, Daryl Hannah, Meg Ryan, Demi Moore, Winona Ryder, Jane Fonda, Bette Davis.

116   Huron, Erie, Apal, Baykal, Cha, Onega, Eyre, Erne, Neagh, Volta, Geneva.

117   Tom Hanks, John Cleese, Tom Cruise, Brad Pitt, Bob Hope, Mel Gibson, Al Pacino, Hugh Grant.

118   Alto, Bass, Chord, Largo, Lento, Opera, Opus, Presto, Rondo, Rubato, Sonato, Tempo, Tenor.

119   E. Elgar
Bizet
Grieg
Verdi

120   O. Cairo
Hanoi
Seoul
Tokyo

121   N. Hymen
Venus
Diana
Woden

122   A. Tango
Polka
Rumba
Samba

123   S. Tyson
Spitz
Senna
Moses

124   A. Indi,
China
Delta
Pan Am

125   N. Monet
Rodin
Munch
Ernst

ANSWERS

126 P.

P	A	R	I	S
I	S	P	A	R
A	R	I	S	**P**
S	P	A	R	I
R	I	S	P	A

128 Y.

B	R	Y	A	N
A	N	B	R	Y
R	Y	A	N	B
N	B	R	Y	A
Y	A	N	B	R

127 I.

I	D	A	H	O
H	O	I	D	A
D	A	H	O	I
O	I	D	A	H
A	H	O	I	D

129 S.

X	A	S	T	E
S	T	E	X	A
E	X	A	S	T
A	S	T	E	X
T	E	X	A	**S**

ANSWERS

130 M.

A	L	M	P	S
M	P	S	A	L
S	A	L	M	P
L	M	P	S	A
P	S	A	L	**M**

132 L.

L	O	T	U	S
T	U	S	L	O
S	L	O	T	U
O	T	U	S	L
U	S	L	O	T

131 F.

U	D	F	R	E
F	R	E	U	D
E	U	D	F	R
D	F	R	E	U
R	E	U	D	**F**

133 W.

E	W	I	S	L
S	L	E	W	I
W	I	S	L	E
L	E	W	I	S
I	S	L	E	**W**

134 Maryland.

135 Winnipeg.

136 Brad Pitt.

137 Jeremiah.

138 Portland.

139 Meatloaf.

140 J. The vowels have been omitted from the surnames and the initial of the first name is in the middle of the box: Tom Cruise, Johnny Depp, Gary Cooper and John Wayne.

141

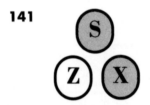

142 T. The cities, without vowels and the initial of the states they are in. Orlando (Florida), Detroit (Michigan), Denver (Colorado) and Dallas (Texas).

143 O. The middle letter of each name is in the middle of the box. Fonda, Hanks, Wayne and Stone.

144 A. The letters outside are consonants of famous tennis players. They are: (top) Borg and Graf, (bottom) Agassi and Cash. The letters inside the triangles are the initials of their nationality. They are Swedish, German, American and Australian respectively.

145 Malaysia and Hong Kong.

146 Chopin and Handel.

147 Exodus and Joshua.

148 Virginia and Delaware,

149 (Calvin) Coolidge and (James) Buchanan.

150 The scientists are: Celsius, Einstein, Bell, Newton.

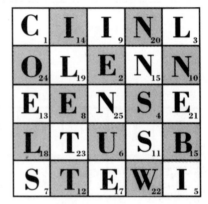

151 The cartoon characters are: Bambi, Cinderella, Pluto and Yogi.

152 The great writers are: Stephen King, Oscar Wilde, William Shakespeare and Jane Austen.

A₂₇	E₆	W₁₇	N₄₂	S₂₉	K₈	L₁₉
R₁₆	N₄₉	M₂₈	N₇	I₁₈	E₄₃	H₃₀
H₅	I₂₆	A₄₁	R₃₈	P₃₅	D₂₀	I₉
E₄₈	A₁₅	E₃₆	**S₁**	J₄₀	A₃₁	A₄₄
L₂₅	P₄	E₃₉	S₃₄	A₃₇	N₁₀	E₂₁
C₁₄	T₄₇	T₂	I₂₃	O₁₂	U₄₅	K₃₂
E₃	L₂₄	S₁₃	S₄₆	E₃₃	W₂₂	G₁₁

153 The stars are: Tom Cruise, Mel Gibson, Robert De Niro, Steve Martin, Whoopi Goldberg, and Jane Fonda.

O₄₅	T₃₂	E₁₁	S₁₆	I₄₇	O₃₀	**T₁**	I₁₄
M₁₀	O₁₇	P₄₆	S₃₁	L₁₂	B₁₅	G₄₈	R₂₉
E₃₃	O₄₄	G₅₅	N₅₈	D₅₁	N₆₂	G₁₃	O₂
N₁₈	E₉	B₅₂	O₆₁	R₅₄	A₅₇	I₂₈	O₄₉
H₄₃	V₃₄	E₅₉	J₅₆	D₆₃	L₅₀	M₃	T₂₄
S₈	R₁₉	A₆₄	E₅₃	F₆₀	D₂₅	R₃₈	N₂₇
E₃₅	W₄₂	B₂₁	U₆	A₃₇	I₄₀	R₂₃	C₄
O₂₀	I₇	M₃₆	N₄₁	E₂₂	R₅	E₂₆	T₃₉

154 The books are: Samuel, Joshua, Mathew, Isaiah, Daniel and Esther.

L₃₀	N₂₇	H₁₀	A₂₃	R₃₆	D₂₅
U₁₁	I₂₂	E₂₉	A₂₆	S₉	S₂₀
I₂₈	E₃₁	O₈	A₂₁	H₂₄	E₃₅
J₇	A₁₂	E₅	A₂	I₁₉	D₁₆
S₃₂	**S₁**	X₁₄	U₁₇	H₃₄	M₃
E₁₃	L₆	T₃₃	U₄	O₁₅	S₁₈

155 The golfers are: Arnold Palmer, Nick Faldo, Tom Watson, Nick Pice and Gary Player.

O₂₃	P₄₄	C₃₃	A₈	O₂₁	R₄₂	N₃₁
K₃₄	**A₁**	T₂₂	Y₄₃	I₃₂	P₇	D₂₀
L₄₅	M₂₄	L₉	R₁₂	C₁₅	N₃₀	A₄₁
R₂	P₃₅	I₁₄	Y₄₇	M₁₀	L₁₉	D₆
W₂₅	A₄₆	E₁₁	K₁₆	N₁₃	G₄₀	O₂₉
R₃₆	N₃	E₄₈	T₂₇	C₃₈	L₅	A₁₈
R₄₉	A₂₆	I₃₇	O₄	F₁₇	S₂₈	E₃₉

156 Malachi
Genesis
Numbers
Ezekiel
The last letter of two
of the four names is
the same.

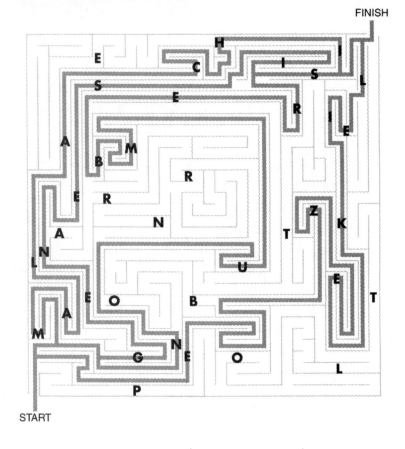

157 Turner
Kilmer
Taylor
Gibson
The first letter of two of
the routes is the same,
and the last letter of
three of the routes is
the same.

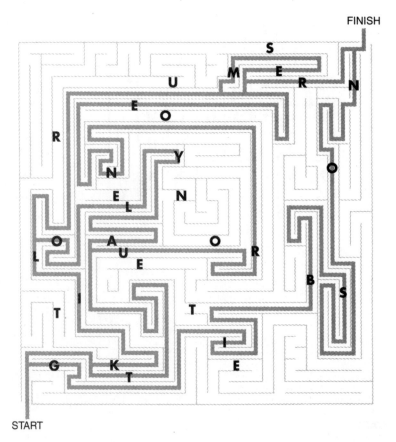

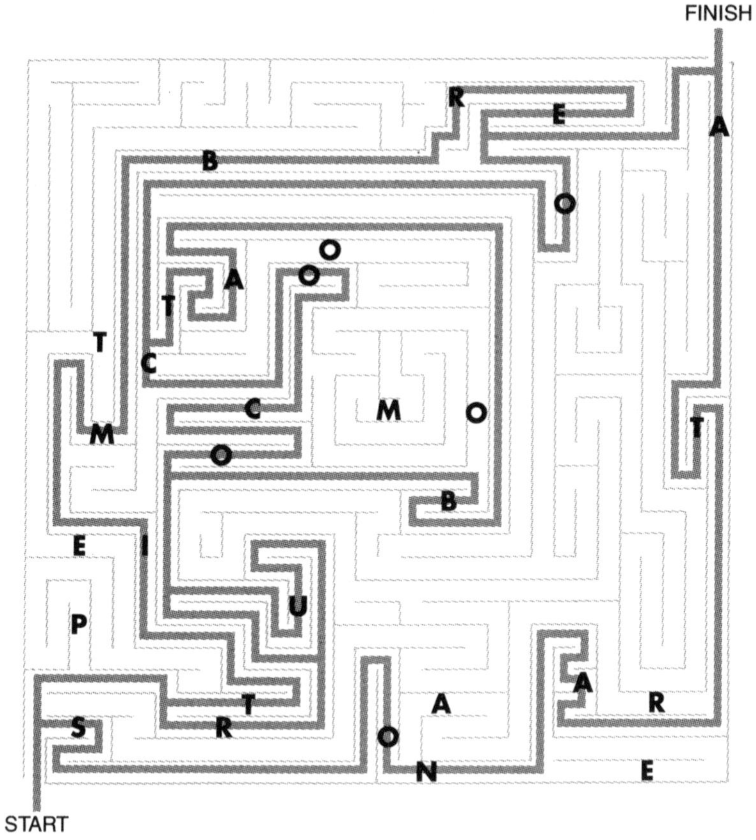

ANSWERS

FINISH

158 Rococo
Rubato
Sonata
Timbre
The first letter of two
of the routes is the
same and the last letter
of two of the routes is
the same.

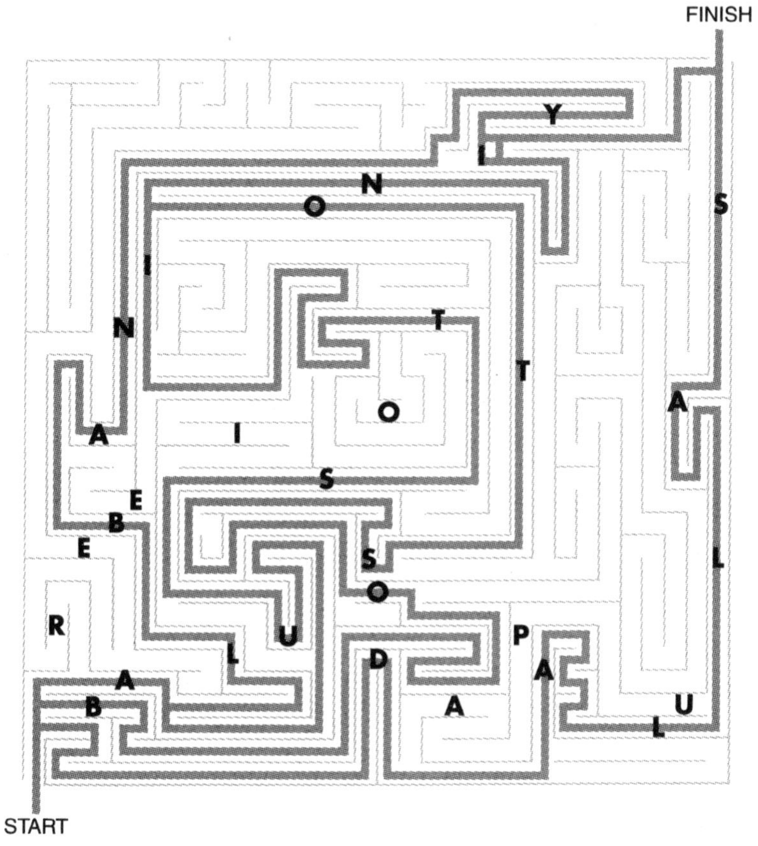

START

FINISH **159** Albany
Austin
Dallas
Boston
The first letter of two
of the routes is the
same and the last letter
of two of the routes is
the same.

START

221

160 Gunnell
Freeman
Johnson
Zelezny
The last letter of two of
the routes is the same.

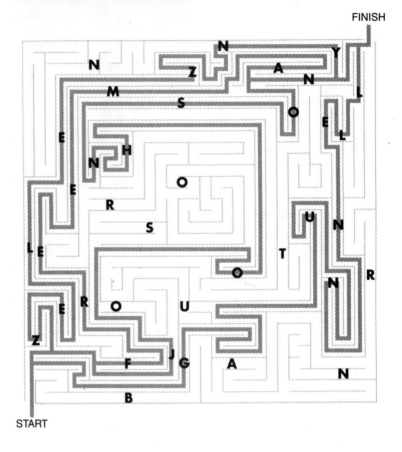

161 Edison
Darwin
Euclid
Pascal
The first letter of two of
the routes is the same
and the last letter of two
of the routes is the same.

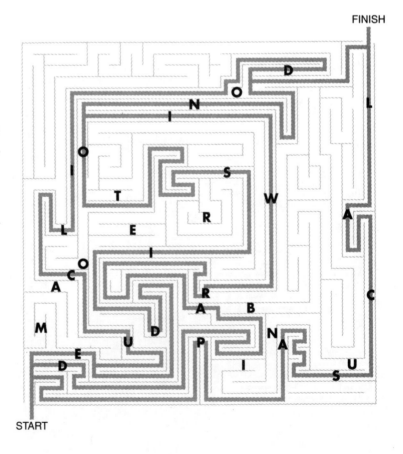

162 1st and 5th – their final position is based on the number of vowels in their names.

163 4th. The finishing order was: 1st, Ferrari; 2nd, Audi; 3rd, Renault; 4th, Ligier, 5th, Mercedes.

164 Bunny was for Dairy, Ermintrude was for Beef and Wilma was for Beef. Take the each name's initial letters' alpha-numeric value; even = dairy, odd = beef.

165 Each value is the sum of Roman numerals in the person's name: Brenda had 500, Axel had 60, Norman had 1000 and Charlie had 151.

166 Mr Becker follows Mr Lewis and then Mr Fischer and then Mr Schultz. The order is based on number of consonants in each person's name.

167 The second letter of the drink is the first letter of each person's name:
Tia Maria for Ian
Vodka for Olga
Whiskey for Harry
Rum for Ursula.

168 The third letter from the end of the car name is the beginning letter of the person's name.
Toyota belongs to Oliver
Rover to Vera
Jaguar to Ursula
Fiat to Irene
Honda to Nigel.

169 12. The number of letters between the alphanumeric position of the first and last letters of each name.

170 Queen Anne. The number of spaces in the alphabet between the second and third letters of each person's name.

171 Zeus.

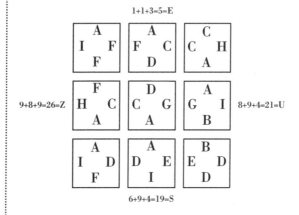

172 U.

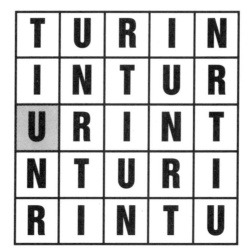

173 Monroe. The penultimate letter of each name is the same.

174 Lidex. The numbers are the value of the roman numerals contained in the other names added together. Lidex should be 561.

175 Triumph. The second letter of the driver and the manfacturer of the car are the same.

176 Van Buren. Neptune was spelled out in the capitalized words of the succeeding lines of the riddle.

177 IBIDIX. The alphanumeric value of the last number, after the dot, is reversed. The previous numbers alternately have their alphanumeric values or the values multiplied by 2.

178 Au = 40%, Ag = 12%. The difference in the alphanumeric values of the first and second letters of each element is doubled.

179

The letters read clockwise from the top left are the consonants in the state capitals and the state's initial is in the middle. Phoenix in Arizona, Oklahoma (City) in Oklahoma, Denver in Colorado and Atlanta in Georgia.

180 Carter
Eisenhower
Johnson
Reagan
Roosevelt

IDENTITY CRISIS
Your name is Christian Alexander Washington.